RADIO PLAYS
from
SHAKESPEARE

Radio Plays
from
Shakespeare

Ten plays by William Shakespeare
adapted for royalty-free performance

by

LEWY OLFSON

Publishers PLAYS, INC. *Boston*

Contents

For

Mary McDavitt

"There's rosemary, that's for remembrance."

HAMLET, IV. V.

Preface

Just as the original plays by William Shakespeare were written for stage performance, the radio adaptations of the plays in this collection were written primarily for actual production. When young people take part in these plays, they become familiar with Shakespeare's work and understand and enjoy plays which have enthralled actors and audiences for more than three hundred years.

These radio adaptations of ten of Shakespeare's most popular plays are designed to introduce young people to the magic of Shakespeare. The plays I have selected are those which I feel will most readily appeal to their minds and imaginations.

While these radio adaptations are streamlined versions of the plays, the essence of these dramatic works is preserved. By highlighting and selecting the most dramatic scenes, and using, for the most part, the wonderful dialogue of Shakespeare, the pace of the scripts is quickened, and the dramatic spirit of the original plays, as well as the magnificence of Shakespeare's language, is retained.

Full *stage* production is usually too demanding for the abilities of teen-age actors, and stage facilities are often inadequate. Participating in these *radio* versions gives young actors the same feeling for the plays, without involving them in the difficulties of staging. By taking the parts of the great characters and reading their lines aloud, young actors are immediately caught up in the dramatic situation of the play and the poetry of the language.

In her fine book, *Pointers on Radio Writing,* Josephina Niggli writes, "There is an old story that William Shakespeare is the greatest radio writer of them all. Not only is his use of description near-perfect for the air, but notice also his concise scenes, the manner in which he opens a play, his method of introducing characters, and his use of the rhymed couplet as a substitute for our music bridges. So, if you want . . . good radio, study Shakespeare."

It is hoped that these radio plays will kindle the interest of young people in reading the original plays in their complete form, and beyond that, the other great plays of Shakespeare.

Technical requirements have been kept to a minimum in these scripts so that the productions can be worked up in very little time. The plays can be presented simply by a group reading aloud with or without a dummy microphone, or as elaborately as desired in a fully equipped "live" studio. At the back of the book there is a "Radio Workshop," with production suggestions that will be of value and interest.

I hope that your pleasure in producing or reading these plays will be as great as mine was in writing them.

Lewy Olfson

RADIO PLAYS
from
SHAKESPEARE

A Midsummer Night's Dream

Characters

THESEUS
EGEUS
HERMIA
LYSANDER
DEMETRIUS

HELENA
OBERON
PUCK
NARRATOR

NARRATOR: Mixing sprites and lovers, fantasy and reality, William Shakespeare wrote a comedy which is truly *A Midsummer Night's Dream*. The play begins in Athens, at the court of Theseus, the Duke of Athens. An Athenian citizen, Egeus, has come before Theseus to complain of his daughter, Hermia. Hermia refuses to marry Demetrius, the man her father has picked for her, and insists on claiming her true love, Lysander. Egeus, Hermia's father, begs the Duke to exercise the ancient Athenian law which would force the girl either to marry the man of her father's choice, or to be banished forever to a convent.

SOUND: *Fanfare.*

EGEUS (*An elderly man, fading on*): Happy be Theseus, our renowned duke!

THESEUS (*Middle-aged*): Thanks, good Egeus: what's the
　　news with thee?

EGEUS: Full of vexation come I, with complaint
　　Against my daughter, Hermia, whom you see
　　With Lysander and Demetrius, here before you.
　　Aye, stand forth, Demetrius. My noble lord,
　　This man hath my consent to marry her.
　　Stand forth, Lysander. And, my gracious Duke,
　　This man hath bewitched the bosom of my child.
　　Thou, thou, Lysander, thou hast given her rhymes,
　　And interchanged love-tokens with my child.
　　With cunning hast thou filched my daughter's heart.
　　Now, my gracious Theseus, Duke of Athens,
　　Be it so she will not here before your Grace
　　Consent to marry with Demetrius,
　　I beg the ancient privilege of Athens,
　　As she is mine, I may dispose of her;
　　Which shall be either to Demetrius,
　　Or to her death, according to our law.

THESEUS: What say you, Hermia? Be advised, fair maid:
　　Demetrius is a worthy gentleman.

HERMIA (*A sweet young woman*): So is Lysander.

THESEUS: In himself he is;
　　But in this kind, wanting your father's voice,
　　The other must be held the worthier.

HERMIA: I do entreat your Grace to pardon me,
　　But I beseech that I may know of you
　　The worst that may befall me in this case,
　　If I refuse to wed Demetrius.

THESEUS: Either to die the death, or to abjure
　　Forever the society of men,
　　And live, grow and die a cloistered nun.

HERMIA: So will I grow, so live, so die, my lord,
  Ere I will yield my heart and freedom up
  Unto his lordship, whose unwished yoke
  My soul consents not to give sovereignty.
THESEUS: Take time to pause; and by the next new moon
  Either prepare to die an early death,
  Or else to wed your father's choice, Demetrius,
  Or on Diana's altar to protest
  For aye austerity and single life.
DEMETRIUS (*A slightly hard young man*): Relent, sweet
  Hermia. And, Lysander, yield
  Thy crazed title to my certain right.
LYSANDER (*A clear young voice*): You have her father's
  love, Demetrius;
  Let me have Hermia's, as hers is mine.
EGEUS: Scornful Lysander! True, he hath my love,
  And what is mine, my love shall render him.
LYSANDER: I am, my lord, as well derived as he,
  As well possessed; my love is more than his,
  And which is more than all these boasts can be,
  I am beloved by beauteous Hermia.
  Why should not I then prosecute my right?
  Demetrius made love to Nedar's daughter,
  Helena, and won that lady's soul.
THESEUS: I must confess that I have heard so much,
  And with Demetrius thought to have spoke thereof;
  But, Demetrius, come; attend me as I walk.
  And come, Egeus. You shall go with me.
  I have some private schooling for you both.
EGEUS: With duty and desire we follow you.
MUSIC: *Romantic theme, in and under.*
NARRATOR: Left alone with her true love, Lysander,

Hermia cannot help but give way to the unhappiness which fills her heart.

LYSANDER: How now, my love? Why is your cheek so pale?
How chance the roses there do fade so fast?

HERMIA: Belike for want of rain, which I could well
Beteem them from the tempest of my eyes.

LYSANDER: Aye me! For aught that I could ever read,
The course of true love never did run smooth.

HERMIA (*Determinedly*): Rather would I die than wed
Demetrius!

LYSANDER: Hear me, Hermia. I have a widow aunt.
From Athens is her house remote seven leagues;
And she respects me as her only son.
There, gentle Hermia, may I marry thee;
And to that place the sharp Athenian law
Cannot pursue us. If thou lov'st me, then,
Steal forth thy father's house tomorrow night.
And in the wood, where I did meet thee once
With Helena, there will I stay for thee.

HERMIA: My good Lysander!
I swear to thee by Cupid's strongest bow,
In that same place thou hast appointed me,
Tomorrow truly will I meet with thee.

LYSANDER: Keep promise, love. Look, here comes Helena!

HERMIA: Good speed, fair Helena!

HELENA (*A sharp-tongued girl, fading on*) : Call you me
fair?
That fair again unsay. Demetrius loves your **fair**.
O, teach me how you look, and with what art
You sway the motion of Demetrius' heart.

HERMIA: I frown upon him, yet he loves me still.

HELENA: O, that your frowns would teach my smiles such
skill.

HERMIA: His folly, Helena, is no fault of mine.

HELENA: None, but your beauty; would that fault were
mine.

HERMIA: Take comfort; he no more shall see my face;
Lysander and myself will fly this place.

LYSANDER: Helen, to you our minds we will unfold.
Tomorrow night shall lovers' flight conceal;
Through Athens' gates have we devised to steal.

HERMIA: And in the wood, where often you and I
Upon faint primrose beds were wont to lie,
There my Lysander and myself shall meet.
But I must go! Farewell, friend: pray for us.
And good luck grant thee thy Demetrius!
Keep word, Lysander. (*Fading*) Till tomorrow night!

LYSANDER: I will, my Hermia. Farewell!

MUSIC: *Pastoral theme, in and under.*

NARRATOR: Thus did the lovers, Hermia and Lysander,
confide in Helena, explaining all the details of their
planned escape from Athens. Helena, however, far from
being the trustworthy friend the lovers think her, immediately begins to turn the matter over in her mind,
comparing Hermia and Lysander's idyllic love with her
own unrequited love for Demetrius.

HELENA: How happy some o'er other some can be!
I am thought as fair as Hermia, but alas!
Demetrius thinks not so. But wait! I see a way!
I will go tell him of fair Hermia's flight;
Then to the wood will he tomorrow night
Pursue her; and for this intelligence,

If I have thanks, it is a dear expense:
But herein mean I to enrich my pain,
To have his sight thither and back again.

MUSIC: *Delightful theme, in and under.*

NARRATOR: As Helena darts off to tell Demetrius about the secret meeting in the wood, another creature, several leagues away, is scheming schemes of his own. He is Oberon, king of the fairies, who, with Queen Titania, rules over the entire forest. Suddenly, Oberon calls for his favorite servant, Puck.

OBERON (*A regal voice*): My gentle Puck, come hither.

PUCK (*A mischievous sprite, fading on*): You called, my lord?

OBERON: Know thou, thy mistress, Queen Titania,
And thy noble lord, King Oberon,
Have lately quarreled in a bitter scene.
Now help me, Puck, to have revenge upon her.
There is a flower, purple with love's wound,
And maidens call it love-in-idleness.
Find me that flower, and bring it hither, Puck.
The juice of it, on sleeping eyelids laid,
Will make a man or woman madly dote
Upon the next live creature that it sees.
Fetch me this herb.

PUCK (*Fading*): I'll put a girdle round the earth in forty minutes.

OBERON: Having once this flower's magic juice,
I'll watch Titania when she is asleep,
And drop the liquor of it on her eyes.
The next thing then she waking looks upon
Be it on lion, bear, or meddling monkey,
She shall pursue it with the soul of love;

Then I can easily remove the charm
With another that I have. But who comes here?
Fortunately, being a fairy, I am invisible;
I shall listen to their conversation.

DEMETRIUS (*Fading on, angrily*): I love thee not, Helena,
therefore pursue me not.
Where is Lysander, and fair Hermia?
You told me they would be here; I have come.
Hence, get thee gone, and follow me no more.

HELENA: You draw me, you hard-hearted adamant.
Leave your power to draw, Demetrius,
And I shall have no power to follow you.

DEMETRIUS: Do I entice you? Do I speak you fair?
Or rather, do I not say I love you not?

HELENA: And even for that do I love you the more.
Neglect me, lose me—only give me leave,
Unworthy as I am, to follow you.

DEMETRIUS (*Fading*): I will not stay thy questions. I am
gone;
And if thou follow me, do not believe
But I shall do thee mischief in the wood.

HELENA: Fie, Demetrius!
I cannot fight for love, as men may do;
I should be woo'd. I was not made to woo.
(*Calling after him*) Demetrius! Demetrius! (*Fading*)
Await me, for I follow!

OBERON (*Laughing*): Fare thee well, girl; ere he do leave
this grove
Thou shalt fly him, and he shall seek thy love.
Good Puck!

PUCK (*Fading on*): Your pleasure, lord?

OBERON: Hast thou the flower?

PUCK: Aye, here it is.

OBERON: I pray thee, give it me.

I'll use a bit of it upon Titania;
Take thou some of it, and seek through this grove.
A sweet Athenian lady is in love
With a disdainful youth: anoint his eyes;
But do it when the next thing he espies
May be the lady. Thou shalt know the man
By the Athenian garments he hath on.
Effect it with some care, that he may prove
More fond on her than she upon her love:
And look thou meet me ere the first cock crow.

PUCK: Fear not, my lord. Your servant shall do so.

MUSIC: *Gay theme, in and under.*

NARRATOR: Thus the good King Oberon contrives with Puck to smooth the unhappy romance of Helena and Demetrius. Unbeknownst to him, however, there is another pair of Athenian lovers in the wood tonight— Hermia and Lysander; and it is these true lovers upon whom Puck happens during his search for the Athenians Oberon had spoken of.

LYSANDER (*Fading on*): Fair Hermia, you faint with wandering in the wood;
And to speak the truth, I have forgot our way:
We'll rest us, Hermia, if you think it good,
And tarry for the comfort of the day.

HERMIA: Be it so, Lysander. Find you out a bed;
For I upon this bank will rest my head.

LYSANDER (*Slightly off mike*): Here is my bed. Sleep give thee all his rest.

HERMIA: With half that wish the wisher's eyes be pressed.

MUSIC: *Dreamy theme, sneak in and hold under.*

NARRATOR: No sooner are the two asleep, when they are discovered by Puck.

PUCK: Night and silence! Who is here?
    Weeds of Athens he doth wear:
    This is he, my master said,
    Despised the Athenian maid.
    And here the maiden sleeping sound
    On the dank and dirty ground.
    Pretty soul, she durst not lie
    Near this lack-love, this kill-courtesy.
    Churl, upon thy eyes I throw
    All the power this charm doth owe.
    When thou wakest, thou shalt love
    The first being which thy sight shall move.
    So awake when I am gone;
    For I must now to Oberon!

MUSIC: *Delightful theme, in and under.*

NARRATOR: And so upon Lysander's sleeping eyelids are placed the drops of Oberon's magic flower, which will cause him to fall in love with the first person he sees upon waking. Since in the normal course of events, that person will be his own true love, Hermia, it would seem no harm is done by Puck's innocent mistake. But at this very moment, Helena is running through the wood in search of Demetrius, and every moment her footsteps lead closer to the grove wherein Lysander and Hermia are asleep.

HELENA (*Breathlessly*): Stay, though thou kill me, sweet Demetrius.

DEMETRIUS (*Slightly off mike, angrily*): I charge thee, hence, and do not haunt me thus!
    (*Fading*) Stay here, on thy peril: I alone will go!

HELENA: Oh, I am out of breath in this fond chase!
The more my prayer, the lesser is my grace.
Happy is Hermia, wheresoe'er she lies.
But who is here? Lysander! On the ground!
Dead? Or asleep? I see no blood, no wound.
Lysander! Good sir, awake!

LYSANDER (*Waking with wonder*): And run through fire
will I for thy sweet sake!
Transparent Helena! Nature shows art,
That through thy bosom makes me see thy heart.
Where is Demetrius? O, how fit a word
Is that vile name to perish on my sword!

HELENA (*Vexed*): Do not say so, Lysander.
What though he love your lady Hermia?
Hermia still loves you: be content.

LYSANDER: Content with Hermia? No, I do repent
The tedious minutes I with her have spent.
Not Hermia, but Helena I love:
Who will not change a raven for a dove?

HELENA: Wherefore was I to this keen mockery born?
When at your hands did I deserve this scorn?
Perforce, Lysander, freely I confess,
I thought you more a gentleman than this.
O, that a lady of one man refused
Should of another be so much abused.
(*Fading angrily*) But fare you well, for I'll have none of
you.

LYSANDER: She sees not Hermia. Hermia, sleep thou there:
And never mayst thou come Lysander near!
Of all be hated, but the most of me.
And, all my powers, address your love and might
To honor Helen and to be her knight.

(*Fading*) Sleep thou there forever, Hermia,
For aught I care.

MUSIC: *Light-hearted theme, in and under.*

NARRATOR: Thus, under the spell of Puck's magic flower, Lysander has fallen out of love with Hermia and into love with Helena. When Hermia wakes and discovers Lysander gone, she begins to search the forest for her lover, and comes upon Demetrius, who, she is convinced, is guilty of harming Lysander in some fashion. Meanwhile, quite unaware of the mischief he has perpetrated, Puck returns to his master, King Oberon.

OBERON: Good Puck, hast thou done my errand?
Hast thou latched the rascal Athenian's eyes
With the love-juice as I bid thee do?

PUCK: I took him sleeping, King Oberon,
And the Athenian woman by his side;
That, when he waked, of force she must be eyed.

OBERON: But stand close: here comes the same Athenian.

PUCK (*Puzzled*): That is the woman, but that is not the man.

OBERON: Shh!

DEMETRIUS (*Fading on*): Oh, why rebuke you him who loves you so?

HERMIA: Now I but chide; but I should use thee worse.
For aught I know, thou hast slain Lysander.
Wherefore was he not beside me when I awoke?
Would he have stolen away? O never, never!
O, tell me truly; hast thou killed him sleeping?

DEMETRIUS: You spend your passion on a mispris'd mood.
I am not guilty of Lysander's blood;
Nor is he dead for aught that I can tell.

HERMIA: I pray thee, tell me then that he is well.

DEMETRIUS: An if I could, what should I get therefore?

HERMIA (*Fading*): A privilege to never see me more.
　　Farewell!

DEMETRIUS: There is no following her in this fierce vein.
　　Here, therefore, I will stay, to sleep awhile
　　Upon this mossy bank, beneath these trees.
　　For debt that bankrupt sleep doth sorrow owe,
　　(*Yawning*) Which now in some slight measure it will
　　　pay. . . . (*His voice trails off*)

OBERON: What hast thou done, Puck? Thou hast mistaken
　　quite,
　　And laid the love-juice on some true love's sight:
　　Of thy misprision must perforce ensue
　　Some true love turned, and not a false turned true.
　　About the wood go swifter than the wind,
　　And Helena of Athens look thou find:
　　All fancy-sick she is with sighs of love.
　　Bring her here: I'll charm Demetrius' eyes
　　Against she do appear.

PUCK (*Fading*): I go!

OBERON: Drops of this purple flower, caress these eyes,
　　That Demetrius may love the first being he espies.
　　But hush—someone comes!

LYSANDER (*Fading on*): Why think you that I should woo
　　in scorn, fair Helen?
　　Scorn and derision never come in tears.

HELENA: These same vows you make to me, Lysander,
　　Lately you have made to Hermia.

LYSANDER: I had no judgement when to her I swore.
　　Demetrius loves her, and loves not you.

HELENA (*Angrily*): Demetrius. . . .

DEMETRIUS (*Waking*): Yet did I hear my name?

O Helen, goddess, divine! O let me kiss
This princess of pure white, this seal of bliss!
HELENA: O spite! O hell! I see you all are bent
To set against me for your merriment.
You both are rivals, and love Hermia;
And now you both mock me with scorn ill-bred,
Pretending to love me in Hermia's stead.
If you were men as men you are in show,
You would not use a gentle lady so.
LYSANDER: Demetrius, you are unkind. You love Hermia;
In Hermia's love I yield you up my part;
And yours of Helena to me bequeath,
Whom I do love, and will do till my death.
DEMETRIUS: Lysander, keep thy lady Hermia;
If e'er I loved her, all that love is gone,
And now to Helen is it home returned.
Look, Lysander; here comes your love.
HERMIA (*Fading on*): At last I find thee here, my good
Lysander.
Wherefore did you leave me as I slept?
LYSANDER: Why should I stay, when love doth press to go?
HERMIA: What pressed you from my side?
LYSANDER: My love for Helena.
HERMIA: You speak not as you think. It cannot be!
HELENA: Lo, she is joined with you in mockery!
Injurious Hermia! Have you too conspired
To bait me with this foul and base derision?
HERMIA: I am amazed at your passionate words.
I scorn you not: it seems that you scorn me.
Lysander, whom do you love?
LYSANDER: My love is Helen's.
DEMETRIUS: And so is mine.

HELENA: O, mock me not, I pray.

HERMIA: And what do they to me, if not mock and scorn?

LYSANDER: Come, Demetrius. It seems that we must try
Whose right of thine or mine is most in Helen.

DEMETRIUS (*Fading*): Gladly will I join to try that right.

HELENA: I will not trust you, treacherous Hermia.
Your hands than mine are quicker for a fray.
(*Fading*) My legs are longer, though, to run away!

HERMIA: I am amazed, and know not what to say!

MUSIC: *Romping theme, in and under.*

NARRATOR: Thus the well-meant efforts of Oberon and
Puck have done nothing but make mischief and confusion among the four Athenian young people. In des-
peration, Oberon calls Puck for the last time, resolved
to untie the tangles of the web he has woven.

OBERON: Puck, Puck, this is thy negligence.
This confusion has resulted either
From your mistakes or from your willful knaveries.

PUCK: Believe me, King of Fairies, I mistook.
Did you not tell me I should know the man
By the Athenian garments he had on?

OBERON: Thou see'st these lovers seek a place to fight;
Hie therefore, Puck, and overcast the night,
And lead these testy rivals so astray
As one come not within another's way.
First, speak to Lysander in Demetrius' voice.
And then play Hermia's voice to Helena.
And from each other look thou lead them thus
Until the four shall fall in slumber deep.
Then crush this herb into Lysander's eye;
To take from thence all error with its might

And make his eyeballs roll with wonted sight.
When they next wake, all this derision
Shall seem a dream and fruitless vision.

PUCK: I shall do it all, m'lord, as you have instructed.

MUSIC: *In and under.*

NARRATOR: Puck having done as Oberon had commanded,
the sun rises the next morning to find the four Athenian
friends sleeping quietly in a shadowed glade. It is the
first of May, and as is his custom, Theseus, the Duke,
is walking through the forest admiring the greenery,
accompanied by old Egeus. In the course of their May-
day stroll, they come upon the sleeping youngsters.

THESEUS: But soft! What nymphs are these?

EGEUS (*Amazed*): My lord, this is my daughter here asleep;
And this, Lysander; this Demetrius is,
This other sleeping lady, Helena!

THESEUS: No doubt they rose up early to observe
The rite of May, even as we; and yet,
I wonder at their being here together.
Yet, wait! Is not this the day
That Hermia should give answer of her choice?

EGEUS: It is, my lord.

THESEUS: Go, bid the huntsmen wake them with their
horns.

SOUND: *Fanfare.*

THESEUS: Good morrow, friends. Saint Valentine is past:
What brings such rivals here in gentle concord?

LYSANDER: My lord, I shall reply amazedly,
Half sleep, half waking: but as yet, I swear,
I cannot truly say how I came here.
But as I think—for truly would I speak—

I came with Hermia hither; our intent
Was to be gone from Athens, where we might,
Without the peril of Athenian law . . .

EGEUS (*Angrily interrupting*): Enough! They would have
    stolen away, my lord;
    Therefore I beg the law upon his head.
    They would have defeated you and me, Demetrius.

DEMETRIUS: My lord, fair Helen told me of their stealth,
    And I in fury hither followed them.
    But, my good lord, I know not by what power,
    My love for Hermia is melted like the snow.
    The object and the pleasure of mine eye
    Is only Helena.

THESEUS: Fair lovers, you are fortunately met.
    Egeus, I will overbear your will.
    For in the temple, by and by, with us
    These couples shall eternally be knit.
    Away with us to Athens; three and three,
    (*Fading*) We'll hold a feast in great solemnity.

DEMETRIUS: These things seem small and undistinguish-
    able.

HERMIA: Methinks I see these things with parted eye,
    When everything seems double.

DEMETRIUS: Are you sure
    That we are awake? It seems to me
    That yet we sleep, we dream. Do you not think
    The Duke was here, and bid us follow him?

HERMIA: Yes, and my father.

LYSANDER: And he did bid us follow to the temple.

HELENA: Why, then, we are awake: let's follow him;
    And by the way let us recount our dreams.

SOUND: *They fade, laughing.*

MUSIC: *Delightful theme, in and under.*

NARRATOR: The web untangled and the knots untied, the four happy young people make their way through the forest, down the hills and into Athens to the temple where they are married. And as they run happily through the forest, the sparkling eyes of Puck are upon them in apology and in blessing.

PUCK: If we shadows have offended,
Think but this, and all is mended:
That you have but slumbered here
While these fancies did appear.
And this weak and idle theme
No more yielding but a dream,
Gentles, do not reprehend:
If you pardon, we will mend.
And, as I am honest Puck,
If we have unearned luck
Now to 'scape the serpent's tongue,
We will make amends ere long;
Else the Puck a liar call:
So, goodnight unto you all.
Give me your hands, if we be friends,
And Puck shall now restore amends.

MUSIC: *Full to finish.*

THE END

The Taming of the Shrew

Characters

KATHARINA MINOLA	TWO SERVANTS
HORTENSIO	A TAILOR
PETRUCHIO	LUCENTIO
BAPTISTA MINOLA	NARRATOR

NARRATOR: Once, in ancient Padua, there lived a lady named Katharina, who was most violent on the subject of men.

KATHARINA (*Loudly*): I'll see thee hanged on Sunday, ere I'll marry thee, or any other!

NARRATOR: And yet, within a few short weeks, that same lady was heard to say:

KATHARINA: Ladies, ladies, it is only meet
We place our hands beneath our husbands' feet.

NARRATOR: How this Italian lady learned a lesson and mended her mind is the subject of one of William Shakespeare's most hilarious comedies, *The Taming of the Shrew.*

MUSIC: *Delightful theme, in and under.*

NARRATOR: Baptista Minola, a wealthy merchant of Padua, has two young daughters, both unmarried. Bianca, the younger of the two, has many suitors for her hand; but Baptista vows that she shall not be wed until he finds a husband for his elder daughter, Katharina. And as Katharina is the sharpest-tongued shrew in all of Italy, it seems that poor Bianca is destined to die unmarried. However, there comes from Verona a hearty man named Petruchio, who is determined to find a wife— and what manner of wife he cares not, so long as she be wealthy. As our story begins, Hortensio, in love with Bianca, encounters his old friend Petruchio, in the streets of Padua.

HORTENSIO: How now! Good friend Petruchio! How do you at Verona?

PETRUCHIO (*A lusty, high-spirited, virile voice*): Signior Hortensio!

HORTENSIO: Tell me now, sweet friend, what happy gale Blows you to Padua here, from old Verona?

PETRUCHIO: Such wind as scatters young men through the world
To seek their fortunes further than at home.
Antonio, my father, is deceased,
And I have thrust myself into this maze,
Haply to wive and thrive as best I may.

HORTENSIO: Petruchio, shall I then come roundly to thee,
And wish thee to a shrewd ill-favour'd wife?
Thou'dst thank me but a little for my counsel;
And yet I'll promise thee she shall be rich.

PETRUCHIO: Signior Hortensio, 'twixt such friends as we,
Few words suffice; and therefore, if thou know
One rich enough to be Petruchio's wife,
Be she as loathsome and as curst and shrewd
As Socrates' Xanthippe, or a worse,

She moves me not, or not removes, at least,
Affection's edge in me, were she as rough
As are the swelling Adriatic seas.
I come to wive it wealthily in Padua;
If wealthily, then happily in Padua.

HORTENSIO: I can, Petruchio, help thee to a wife
With wealth enough, and young and beauteous;
Her only fault—and that is faults enough—
Is, that she is intolerable shrewd.
I would not wed her for a mine of gold!

PETRUCHIO: Hortensio, peace! Thou know'st not gold's
effect:
Tell me her father's name, and 'tis enough.

HORTENSIO: Her father is Baptista Minola,
An affable and courteous gentleman;
Her name is Katharina Minola,
Renown'd in Padua for her scolding tongue.

PETRUCHIO: I will not sleep, Hortensio, till I see her!

HORTENSIO: Thou'lt undertake to woo curst Katharine?

PETRUCHIO: Yea, and to marry her, if her dowry please.
Why came I hither but to that intent?
Think you a little din can daunt mine ears?
Have I not in my time heard lions roar?
And do you tell me of a woman's tongue,
That gives not half so great a blow to hear
As will a chestnut in a farmer's fire? (*Laughs hilari-
ously.*)

HORTENSIO: The motion's good indeed, and be it so:
Petruchio, I shall be your *ben venuto.*

MUSIC: *Light-hearted theme, in and under.*

NARRATOR: And so Petruchio, determined to wed the
shrew, Katharina, if she have a large enough dowry, goes

off to her father's house—where, at the moment, that very father's life is being made miserable by that very shrew!

KATHARINA (*Off mike, shouting*): No!

SOUND: *Crash of dishes.*

KATHARINA (*Off mike*): No!

SOUND: *Crash.*

KATHARINA (*Off mike*): No!

BAPTISTA (*Fading on*): Was ever gentleman thus grieved as I?

But who comes here?

HORTENSIO (*Fading on*): Good morrow, neighbor Baptista.

BAPTISTA: Good morrow, neighbor Hortensio. God save you, gentlemen.

PETRUCHIO: And you, good sir. Pray, have you not a daughter,

Call'd Katharina, fair and virtuous?

BAPTISTA: I have a daughter, sir, call'd Katharina.

PETRUCHIO: I am a gentleman of Verona, sir,

That, hearing of her beauty and her wit,

Her affability and bashful modesty,

Her wondrous qualities and mild behavior,

Am bold to show myself a forward guest

Within your house, to make mine eye the witness

Of that report which I so oft have heard.

BAPTISTA (*Dryly*): As for my daughter Katharine, this I know,

She is not for your turn, the more my grief.

PETRUCHIO: Signior Baptista, my business asketh haste,

And every day I cannot come to woo.

Then tell me, if I get your daughter's love,

What dowry shall I have with her to wife?

BAPTISTA: After my death the one half of my lands,
And in possession twenty thousand crowns.

PETRUCHIO: And, for that dowry, I'll assure her of
Her widowhood, be it that she survive me,
In all my lands and leases whatsoever.
Let specialties be therefore drawn between us,
That covenants may be kept on either hand.

BAPTISTA: Ay, when the special thing is well obtain'd,
That is, her love; for that is all in all.

PETRUCHIO: Why, that is nothing; for I tell you, father,
I am peremptory as she proud-minded;
And where two raging fires meet together
They do consume the thing that feeds their fury:
So I to her, and so she yields to me;
For I am rough, and woo not like a babe.

BAPTISTA: Well mayst thou woo, and happy be thy speed!
But be thou arm'd for some unhappy words.

PETRUCHIO: Now, by the world, it is a lusty wench!
O! How I long to have some chat with her.

BAPTISTA (*Fading*): Hortensio, come. Petruchio, wait thou
here.
I shall send my daughter Kate to you.

PETRUCHIO (*Calling after him*): I pray you do; I will attend her here,
(*Confidential, in close*) And woo her with some spirit
when she comes.
Say that she rail; why then I'll tell her plain
She sings as sweetly as a nightingale.
Say that she frown; I'll say she looks as clear
As morning roses newly wash'd with dew:
Say she be mute; then I'll commend her tongue.
If she do bid me pack, I'll give her thanks,

As though she bid me stay by her a week.
If she deny to wed, I'll crave the day
When I shall ask the banns, and when be married.
But here she comes; and, now, Petruchio, speak.
Good-morrow, Kate; for that's your name, I hear.

KATHARINA (*A shrew; fading on*): Well have you heard,
but something hard of hearing:
They call me Katharine that do talk of me.

PETRUCHIO: You lie, in faith; for you are call'd plain Kate,
And bonny Kate, and sometimes Kate the curst;
But Kate, the prettiest Kate in Christendom!
Take this of me, Kate of my consolation;
Hearing thy mildness praised in every town,
Myself am moved to woo thee for my wife.

KATHARINA: Moved! In good time! Let him that moved
you hither
Remove you hence.

PETRUCHIO: Come, come, you wasp; i' faith, you are too
angry.

KATHARINA: If I be waspish, best beware my sting.

PETRUCHIO: Good Kate, I am a gentleman.

KATHARINA: That I'll try!

SOUND: *Slap.*

PETRUCHIO: O! I swear I'll cuff you if you strike again.

KATHARINA: If you strike me, you are no gentleman.

PETRUCHIO: Nay, come, Kate, come; you must not look
so sour.

KATHARINA: It is my fashion when I see a crab.

PETRUCHIO: Why, here's no crab, and therefore look not
sour.

KATHARINA: There is, there is.

PETRUCHIO: Then show it me.

KATHARINA: Had I a glass, I would.

PETRUCHIO: Nay, hear you, Kate: in sooth, you 'scape not
so.

KATHARINA: I chafe you, if I tarry: let me go.

PETRUCHIO: Nay, not a whit. I find you passing gentle.
'Twas told me you were rough and coy and sullen,
And now I find report a very liar.
For thou art pleasant, gamesome, passing courteous,
But slow in speech, yet sweet as spring-time flowers:
Nor hast thou pleasure to be cross in talk,
But thou with mildness entertain'st thy wooers.
O slanderous world, that doth report Kate wrongly!

KATHARINA: Where did you study all this goodly speech?

PETRUCHIO: It is extempore, from my mother-wit.

KATHARINA: A witty mother! Witless else her son.

PETRUCHIO: Come, Kate: setting all this chat aside,
Thus in plain terms: your father hath consented
That you shall be my wife; your dowry 'greed on;
And will you, nill you, I will marry you.
Now, Kate, I am a husband for your turn;
For, by this light, whereby I see thy beauty,
Thou must be married to no man but me.
For I am he am born to tame you, Kate;
And bring you from a wild Kate to a Kate,
Conformable as other household Kates.
Here comes your father: never make denial;
I must and will have Katharine to my wife.

BAPTISTA (*Fading on*): Now, Signior Petruchio, how speed
you with my daughter?

PETRUCHIO: How but well, sir? How but well?
It were impossible I should speed amiss.

BAPTISTA: Why, how now, daughter Katharine! In your dumps?

KATHARINA (*Hotly*): Call you me daughter? Now I promise you:
You have show'd a tender fatherly regard,
To wish me wed to one half lunatic!

PETRUCHIO: Father, 'tis thus: yourself and all the world,
That talk'd of her, have talk'd amiss of her:
For she's not forward, but modest as the dove;
She is not hot, but temperate as the morn.
And to conclude, we have 'greed so well together,
That upon Sunday is the wedding day.

KATHARINA: I'll see thee hang'd on Sunday first!

HORTENSIO: Hark, Petruchio: she says she'll see thee hang'd first.

PETRUCHIO: Be patient, gentlemen; I choose her for myself:
If she and I be pleased, what's that to you?
'Tis bargain'd, 'twixt us twain, being alone,
That she shall still be curst in company.
I tell you, 'tis incredible to believe
How much she loves me! O, the kindest Kate!
She hung about my neck, and kiss on kiss
She vied so fast, protesting oath on oath,
That in a twink she won me to her love.
Give me thy hand, Kate: I will unto Venice
To buy apparel 'gainst the wedding-day.
Provide the feast, father, and bid the guests;
I will be sure my Katharine shall be fine.

BAPTISTA: I know not what to say; but give me your hands.
God send you joy, Petruchio; 'tis a match.

HORTENSIO: Amen, say I; and I will be a witness.

PETRUCHIO: Father, and wife, and Hortensio, adieu.

    I will to Venice; Sunday comes apace:

    We will have rings, and things, and fine array:

    And, kiss me, Kate, we will be married o'Sunday.

MUSIC: *Rollicking theme, in and under.*

NARRATOR: And so was the unwilling shrew, Katharina Minola, affianced to the determined Petruchio. A week passes, and the day of the wedding arrives. But as the hour of the ceremony approaches, the bridegroom, Petruchio, is still not returned from Venice.

BAPTISTA: Signior Hortensio, this is the 'pointed day

    That Katharine and Petruchio should be married,

    And yet we hear not of our son-in-law.

    What will be said? What mockery will it be

    To want the bridegroom when the priest attends

    To speak the ceremonial rites of marriage!

    What says Hortensio to this shame of ours?

KATHARINA (*Furiously*): No shame but mine; I must, forsooth, be forced

    To give my hand, opposed against my heart

    Unto a mad-brain rudesby, full of spleen;

    Who woo'd in haste, and means to wed at leisure.

    I told you, I, he was a frantic fool.

    He'll woo a thousand, 'point the day of marriage,

    Make feasts, invite friends, and proclaim the banns;

    Yet never means to wed where he hath woo'd.

    Now must the world point at poor Katharine,

    And say, "Lo! There is mad Petruchio's wife,

    If it would please him come and marry her!"

HORTENSIO: Patience, good Katharine, and Baptista too.

    Upon my life, Petruchio means but well,

Whatever fortune stays him from his word.

Though he be blunt, I know him passing wise;

Though he be merry, yet withal he's honest.

KATHARINA (*Fading, weeping*): Would Katharine had never seen him, though!

BAPTISTA (*Sadly*): Go, girl, I cannot blame thee now to weep,

For such an injury would vex a very saint,

Much more a shrew of thy impatient humor.

SERVANT (*Fading on*): Master, master! News! Old news, and such news as you never heard of!

BAPTISTA: Is it new and old too? How may that be?

SERVANT: Why, Petruchio is coming, in a new hat and an old jerkin; a pair of old breeches, thrice turned; a pair of boots that have been candle-cases, one buckled, another laced; an old rusty sword with a broken hilt, and chapeless; with two broken points: his horse hipped with an old mothy saddle and stirrups of no kindred.

HORTENSIO: 'Tis some odd humor pricks him to this fashion;

Yet oftentimes he goes but mean-apparell'd.

BAPTISTA: I am glad he is come, howso'er he comes.

PETRUCHIO (*Fading on*): Come, where be these gallants? Who is at home?

BAPTISTA: You are welcome, sir.

PETRUCHIO: And yet I come not well.

But where is Kate? Where is my lovely bride?

The morning wears, 'tis time we were at church.

BAPTISTA: See not your bride in these unreverent robes:

Go to my chamber; put on clothes of mine.

PETRUCHIO: Not I, believe me: thus I'll visit her.

BAPTISTA: But thus, I trust, you will not marry her.

PETRUCHIO: Good sooth, even thus; therefore ha' **done** with words:
To me she's married, not unto my clothes.
Could I repair what she will wear in me
As I can change these poor accoutrements,
'Twere well for Kate and better for myself!
Come!

MUSIC: *Delightful theme, in and under.*

NARRATOR: Adding to the injury of attending his own wedding in rags, Petruchio proceeds to swear at the priest and curse and bellow throughout the ceremony. Immediately after he and Kate are married, he announces to the assembled company that he and his wife cannot stay to enjoy the wedding feast . . . which news greatly upsets the new bride.

PETRUCHIO: Gentlemen and friends, I thank you for your pains:
I know you think to dine with me today,
But so it is, my haste doth call me hence,
And therefore here I mean to take my leave.

BAPTISTA: Is't possible you will away tonight?

PETRUCHIO: I must away today, before night come.
And, honest company, I thank you all,
That have beheld me give away myself
To this most patient, sweet and virtuous wife.

BAPTISTA: Let us entreat you stay till after dinner.

PETRUCHIO: It may not be.

HORTENSIO: Let me entreat you.

PETRUCHIO: It cannot be.

KATHARINA: Let me entreat you.

PETRUCHIO: I am content.

KATHARINA: Are you content to stay?

PETRUCHIO: I am content you shall entreat me stay,
But yet not stay, entreat me how you can.

KATHARINA: Now, if you love me, stay.

PETRUCHIO: Servant, my horse!

KATHARINA: Nay, then,
Do what thou canst, I will not go today;
No, nor tomorrow, not till I please myself.
The door is open, sir; there lies your way.
For me, I'll not be gone till I please myself.

PETRUCHIO: O Kate! Content thee. Prithee, be not angry.

KATHARINA: I will be angry. What hast thou to do?
Father, be quiet; he shall stay my leisure.
Gentleman, forward to the bridal dinner:
I see a woman may be made a fool,
If she had not a spirit to resist.

PETRUCHIO: They shall go forward, Kate, at thy command.
Obey the bride, you that attend on her.
But for my bonny Kate, she must with me.
Nay, look not big, nor stamp, nor stare, nor fret;
I will be master of what is mine own.
She is my goods, my chattels; she is my house,
My horse, my ox, my ass, my anything.
And here she stands, touch her whoever dare.
Fear not, sweet wench; they shall not touch thee, Kate.
I'll buckler thee against a million!

MUSIC: *Romping theme, in and under.*

NARRATOR: Thus does Petruchio, a man of great determination, begin the taming of his shrew. After a long
journey, which completely tires Katharina, they reach
Petruchio's house, where they prepare for supper. At

least, Katharina prepares—not realizing that her husband is determined that she shall not eat a bite until her temper is tamed!

PETRUCHIO: Come, Kate, sit down; I know you have a stomach.

Will you give thanks, sweet Kate, or else shall I?

What's this? Mutton?

SERVANT (*Slightly off mike*): Ay.

PETRUCHIO: Who brought it?

SERVANT: I.

PETRUCHIO: 'Tis burnt; and so is all the meat!

What dogs are these! Where is the rascal cook?

How durst you, villains, bring it from the dresser,

And serve it thus to me that love it not?

SOUND: *Crash of table china.*

PETRUCHIO: There, take it to you, trenchers, cups, and all.

You heedless joltheads and unmanner'd slaves!

KATHARINA (*Tired and hungry*): I pray you, husband, be not so disquiet.

The meat was well if you were so contented.

PETRUCHIO: I tell thee, Kate, 'twas burnt and dried away;

And better 'twere that both of us did fast,

Than feed upon such over-roasted flesh.

Be patient; tomorrow 't shall be mended,

And for this night, we'll fast for company.

MUSIC: *Light-hearted theme, in and under.*

NARRATOR: But refusing Katharine her supper is only the beginning of Petruchio's plan.

PETRUCHIO: Thus have I politicly begun my reign,

And 'tis my hope to end successfully.

My falcon now is sharp and passing empty,

And till she stoop she must not be full-gorged.

She eat no meat today, nor none shall eat;
Last night she slept not, nor tonight she shall not.
As with the meat, some undeserved fault
I'll find about the making of the bed;
And here I'll fling the pillow, there the bolster,
This way the coverlet, another way the sheets:
And in conclusion she shall watch all night.
And if she chance to nod, I'll rail and brawl,
And with the clamor keep her still awake.
This is a way to kill a wife with kindness;
And thus I'll curb her mad and headstrong humor.
He that knows better how to tame a shrew,
Now let him speak: 'tis charity to show.

MUSIC: *In and under.*

NARRATOR: Needless to say, this sharp treatment was having its effect on Katharina.

KATHARINA: The more my wrong, the more his spite appears.
What, did he marry me to famish me?
Beggars, that come unto my father's door,
Upon entreaty have a present alms;
If not, elsewhere they meet with charity.
But I, who never knew how to entreat,
Nor never needed that I should entreat,
Am starv'd for meat, giddy for lack of sleep;
With oaths kept waking, and with brawling fed.
And that which spites me more than all these wants,
He does it under name of perfect love!

PETRUCHIO (*Fading on*): How fares my Kate?

KATHARINA (*Dismally*): Faith, as cold as can be.

PETRUCHIO: Pluck up thy spirits; look cheerfully upon me.

    Here, love; thou seest how diligent I am,
    To dress thy meat myself and bring it thee.
    I am sure, sweet Kate, this kindness merits thanks.
    What! Not a word? Nay then, thou lovest it not,
    And all my pains is sorted to no proof.
    Here, servant, take away this dish of meat.

KATHARINA: I pray you, servant, let it stand.

PETRUCHIO: The poorest service is repaid with thanks,
    And so shall mine, before you touch the meat.

KATHARINA (*Coldly*): I thank you, sir.

PETRUCHIO: But put aside your supper, lovely Kate.
    For here's the tailor, come with clothes for thee.
    Come, tailor, let us see these ornaments.
    Lay forth the gown, and let us see the cap.

TAILOR: Here is the cap your worship did bespeak.

PETRUCHIO (*Feigning anger*): Why, this was moulded on
    a porringer!
    Away with it! Come, let me have a bigger.

KATHARINA (*Determined*): I'll have no bigger: this doth
    fit the time,
    And gentlewomen wear such caps as these.

PETRUCHIO: When you are gentle, you shall have one too;
    And not till then.

KATHARINA: Why, sir, I trust I may have leave to speak,
    And speak I will; I am no child, no babe.
    Love me or love me not, I like the cap,
    And it I will have, or I will have none.

PETRUCHIO: As thou speak'st, Kate; thou shalt have none.
    Now, tailor, let us see the gown thou'st brought.
    O mercy, Lord! What masking stuff is here?
    What! Up and down, carv'd like an apple tart?
    Here's snip, and nip, and cut, and slish, and slash.

TAILOR (*Meekly*): You bid me make it orderly and well,
According to the fashion and the time.

PETRUCHIO: Marry, and did: but if you be remember'd,
I did not bid you mar it to the time.
I'll none of it: hence! Make your best of it!

TAILOR (*Fading hastily*): Ay, ay, my lord! So please you!
Yes, my lord!

KATHARINA (*Plaintively*): I never saw a better fashion'd gown,
More quaint, more pleasing, nor more commendable.

PETRUCHIO: Well, come, my Kate; we will unto your father's,
Even in these honest mean habiliments.
What if we are not deck'd in newest clothes?
Is the adder better than the eel
Because his painted skin contents the eye?
O, no, good Kate; neither art thou the worse
For this poor furniture and mean array.
And therefore frolic: we will hence forthwith,
To feast and sport us at thy father's house.
Let's see; I think 'tis now some seven o'clock,
And well we may come there by dinner time.

KATHARINA: I dare assure you, sir, 'tis almost two;
And 'twill be supper-time ere you come there.

PETRUCHIO (*Firmly*): Look, what I speak, or do, or think to do,
You are still crossing it. But mark me well:
I will not go today; and ere I do,
It shall be what o'clock *I say it is!*

MUSIC: *Romping theme, in and under.*

NARRATOR: Finally Petruchio considers that his wife is
subdued sufficiently for her to be presented at the home

of her father once again. But even on the journey, the taming continues. In the inns. . . .

KATHARINA: 'Tis cold!

PETRUCHIO (*Calmly*): 'Tis hot!

KATHARINA (*Angrily*): 'Tis cold!

PETRUCHIO (*Warningly*): 'Tis hot! . . .

KATHARINA (*Resignedly*): 'Tis . . . hot.

NARRATOR: And on the roads. . . .

PETRUCHIO: Come on, i' God's name; once more toward our father's.

Good Lord, how bright and goodly shines the moon!

KATHARINA: The moon! The sun! It is not moonlight now.

PETRUCHIO: I say it is the moon that shines so bright.

KATHARINA: I know it is the sun that shines so bright.

PETRUCHIO: Now, by my mother's son, and that's myself,

It shall be moon, or star, or what I list,

Or ere I journey to your father's house.

(*Calling out*) Go, one, and fetch our horses back again!

Evermore cross'd and cross'd; nothing but cross'd!

KATHARINA (*Tiredly*): Forward, I pray, since we have come so far,

And be it moon, or sun, or what you please.

And if you please to call it a rush-candle,

Henceforth I vow it shall be so for me.

PETRUCHIO: I say it is the moon.

KATHARINA: I know it is the moon.

PETRUCHIO: Nay, then, you lie; it is the blessed sun.

KATHARINA: Then God be bless'd, it is the blessed sun:

But sun it is not when you say it is not,

And the moon changes even as your mind.

What you will have it nam'd, even that it is;

And so, it shall be so for Katharine.

MUSIC: *Light-hearted theme, in and under.*

NARRATOR: When they finally reach the home of old Baptista Minola, they find a double marriage being celebrated. Hortensio, who had given up waiting for Katharina's younger sister, Bianca, is married to a widow. And Bianca, Baptista's younger daughter, has taken a young lord named Lucentio for her husband. After dinner, the men sit before the fire, discussing their wives, and old Baptista turns to Petruchio.

BAPTISTA: Now, in good sadness, son Petruchio,

I think thou hast the veriest shrew of all.

PETRUCHIO: Well, I say no: and therefore, for assurance,

Let's each one send unto his wife;

And he whose wife is most obedient

To come at first when he doth send for her,

Shall win the wager which we will propose.

HORTENSIO: Content. What is the wager?

LUCENTIO: Twenty crowns.

HORTENSIO: Who shall begin?

LUCENTIO: That will I.

Servant, bid my lady, Bianca, come to me.

SERVANT (*Fading*): I will, my lord.

BAPTISTA: Son, I will be your half, Bianca comes.

LUCENTIO: I'll have no halves; I'll bear it all myself.

How now! What news?

SERVANT (*Slightly off mike*): Sir, my mistress sends you word

That she is busy and she cannot come.

PETRUCHIO (*Laughing*): How! She is busy, and she cannot come.

Is that an answer?

HORTENSIO: Ay, and a kind one too:
  Pray God, sir, your wife send you not a worse.
PETRUCHIO: I hope, better.
HORTENSIO: Servant, go thou and entreat *my* wife
  To come to me forthwith.
PETRUCHIO: O ho! "Entreat her."
  Nay, then she must needs come.
HORTENSIO (*Laughing*): I am afraid, sir,
  Do what you can, yours will not be entreated.
  Now where's my wife?
SERVANT (*Slightly off mike*): She says you have some
    goodly jest in hand:
  She will not come: she bids you come to her.
PETRUCHIO: Worse and worse; she will not come! O vile,
  Intolerable, not to be endur'd!
  Sirrah! Go to your mistress, Katharine, and say,
  I command her come to me.
HORTENSIO: I know her answer.
PETRUCHIO: What?
HORTENSIO: She will not.
PETRUCHIO: The fouler fortune mine, and there an end.
BAPTISTA (*Amazed*): Now, by my holidame, here comes
  Katharina!
KATHARINA (*Fading on*): What is your will, sir, that you
  send for me?
PETRUCHIO: Where is your sister, and Hortensio's wife?
KATHARINA: They sit conferring by the parlor fire.
PETRUCHIO: Go, fetch them hither: if they deny to come,
  Swinge me them soundly forth unto their husbands.
  Away, I say, and bring them hither straight.
LUCENTIO: Here is a wonder, if you talk of wonder.
HORTENSIO: And so it is. I wonder what it bodes.

PETRUCHIO: Marry, peace it bodes, and love, and quiet life.
BAPTISTA: Now fair befall thee, good Petruchio!
  For she is changed, as she had never been.
PETRUCHIO: Nay, I will win my wager better yet,
  And show more signs of her obedience.
  See where she comes, and brings your froward wives
  As prisoners to her womanly persuasion.
  Katharine, I charge thee, tell these headstrong women
  What duty they do owe their lords and husbands.
KATHARINA (*Gently*): Fie, fie! Unknit that threatening un-
  kind brow,
  Dear Sister Bianca, and Hortensio's wife.
  It blots thy beauty as frosts do bite the meads.
  Thy husband is thy lord, thy life, thy keeper,
  Thy head, thy sovereign; one that cares for thee,
  And for thy maintenance, commits his body
  To painful labor both by sea and land,
  Whilst thou liest warm at home, secure and safe;
  And craves no other tribute at thy hands
  But love, fair looks, and true obedience;
  Too little payment for so great a debt.
  Such duty as the subject owes the prince,
  Even such a woman oweth her husband.
  I am asham'd that women are so simple
  To offer war where they should kneel for peace,
  Or seek for rule, supremacy, and sway,
  When they are bound to serve, love, and obey.
  Come, come, you froward and unable worms!
  My mind hath been as big as one of yours,
  To bandy word for word and frown for frown;
  But now I see our lances are but straws,
  Our strength as weak, our weakness past compare,

That seeming to be most which we indeed least are.
Then vail your stomachs, for it is no boot,
And place your hands below your husband's foot:
In token of which duty, if he please,
My hand is ready; may it do him ease.

PETRUCHIO (*Heartily*): Why, there's a wench! Come on, and kiss me, Kate!

HORTENSIO: Now, go thy ways; thou hast tam'd a curst shrew.

BAPTISTA (*Wonderingly*): 'Tis a wonder, by your leave, she will be tam'd so.

MUSIC: *Rollicking theme, full to finish.*

THE END

Much Ado About Nothing

Characters

BEATRICE	DON PEDRO OF ARRAGON
BENEDICK	CLAUDIO
LEONATO	URSULA
A MESSENGER	NARRATOR
HERO	

NARRATOR: Beatrice and Benedick, two young people of the Italian nobility, hated each other with an intense loathing that was not to be surpassed. She said of him:

BEATRICE: Benedick? He is like a disease. Why, he's a pestilence!

NARRATOR: And he said of her:

BENEDICK: Beatrice? I would my horse had the speed of her tongue!

NARRATOR: How they hated, and how they came to love, is the meat and matter of William Shakespeare's rousing comedy, *Much Ado About Nothing*.

MUSIC: *Light-hearted theme, in and under.*

NARRATOR: Don Pedro, kindly Prince of Arragon, returns to Messina after a war in which he has emerged victorious. In company with two young lords, Benedick and

41

Claudio, he prepares to visit with his old friend, Leonato. He sends before him a messenger, bearing a letter to Leonato, telling of his coming. As the play begins, Leonato is talking of Don Pedro's arrival with the messenger, while Hero, Leonato's daughter, and Beatrice, his niece, listen.

LEONATO (*An old, kindly man*): I learn from this letter that Don Pedro of Arragon comes this night to Messina.

MESSENGER: Ay, Signior Leonato. He is very near by this; he was not three leagues off when I left him.

LEONATO: You say that Don Pedro hath bestowed much honor on a young Florentine called Claudio?

MESSENGER: That Claudio hath borne himself beyond the promise of his age, doing in the figure of a lamb, the feats of a lion.

BEATRICE (*A sharp-tongued girl with a sense of humor*): Tell me, Messenger, I pray, is "Signior Mountanto" returned from the wars or no?

MESSENGER: I know none of that name, lady.

HERO (*A sweet young girl*): My cousin Beatrice means Signior Benedick of Padua.

MESSENGER: Oh, he is returned. He hath done good service in these wars, for he is a good soldier, too, lady.

BEATRICE: And a good soldier to a lady; but what is he to a lord?

MESSENGER: A lord to a lord, a man to a man; stuffed with all honorable virtues.

BEATRICE: Indeed, he is no less than a stuffed man!

LEONATO: You must not, sir, mistake my niece. There is a kind of merry war betwixt Signior Benedick and her: they never meet but there's a skirmish of wit between them.

BEATRICE: In our last conflict four of his five wits went halting off, and now is the whole man governed with one. Who is his companion now? He hath every month a new sworn brother. He wears his faith but as the fashion of his hat; it ever changes with the next block.

MESSENGER: I see, lady, the gentleman is not in your books.

BEATRICE: No; an he were, I would burn my study. But I pray you, who is his companion?

MESSENGER: He is most in the company of the right noble Claudio.

BEATRICE: God help the noble Claudio!

MESSENGER: But look you; Don Pedro is approached!

SOUND: *Flourish of trumpets.*

DON PEDRO (*Fading on*): Good Signior Leonato, are you come to meet your trouble? The fashion of the world is to avoid cost, and you encounter it!

LEONATO: Never came trouble to my house in the likeness of your Grace.

DON PEDRO: I think this is your daughter, Hero. Be happy, lady, for you are like an honorable father.

HERO: I thank you, your Grace.

DON PEDRO: Leonato, you remember Signior Benedick? And this is the faithful Florentine, Lord Claudio.

CLAUDIO (*A gentle youth*): Signior Leonato.

BENEDICK (*A young man with a keen-edged tongue*): If Signior Leonato be the Lady Hero's father, she would not have his head on her shoulders for all Messina, as like him as she is.

BEATRICE: I wonder that you will still be talking, Signior Benedick. Nobody marks you.

BENEDICK (*As though surprised*): Why, my dear Lady Disdain! Are you yet living?

BEATRICE: Is it possible Disdain should die while she hath such meet food to feed it as Signior Benedick?

BENEDICK: It is certain that I am loved of all ladies, only you excepted; and I would I could find in my heart that I had not a hard heart, for truly I love none.

BEATRICE: A dear happiness to women; they would else have been troubled with a pernicious suitor. I thank God and my cold blood, I am of your humor for that. I had rather hear my dog bark at a crow than a man swear he loves me.

BENEDICK: God keep your ladyship still in that mind! So some gentleman or other shall scape a predestinate scratched face.

BEATRICE: Scratching could not make it worse, an 'twere such a face as yours.

DON PEDRO: Signior Claudio and Signior Benedick, my dear friend Leonato hath invited you all. I tell him we shall stay here at least a month; and he heartily prays some occasion may detain us longer.

LEONATO: Please your Grace lead on?

DON PEDRO (*Fading*): Your hand, Leonato; we will go together.

MUSIC: *Delightful theme, in and under.*

NARRATOR: As Leonato had predicted, Beatrice and Benedick were at once at each other's throats. But the young Claudio falls deeply in love with Leonato's fair daughter, Hero, and as soon as he and his friend Benedick are alone, Claudio questions him.

CLAUDIO: Benedick, didst thou note the daughter of Signior Leonato?

BENEDICK: I noted her not; but I looked on her.

CLAUDIO: Is she not a modest young lady?

BENEDICK: Why, i' faith, methinks she's too low for a high praise and too little for a great praise.

CLAUDIO: Thou thinkest I am in sport; I pray thee tell me truly how thou lik'st her.

BENEDICK: Would you buy her, that you inquire after her?

CLAUDIO: Can the world buy such a jewel? In mine eye, she is the sweetest lady that ever I looked on.

BENEDICK: I can see yet without spectacles and I see no such matter: there's her cousin, who, if she were not possessed with a fury, exceeds her as much in beauty as the first of May doth the last of December. But I hope you have no intent to turn husband, have you?

CLAUDIO: I would scarce trust myself, though I had sworn to the contrary, if Hero would be my wife.

BENEDICK: Is't come to this? In faith, shall I never see a bachelor of three-score again? Look! Don Pedro is returned to seek you.

DON PEDRO (*Fading on*): What secret hath held you here, that you followed not to Leonato's?

BENEDICK: Count Claudio, our friend, is in love. In love! With who? Mark how short his answer is. With Hero, Leonato's short daughter.

CLAUDIO: If this were so, so it were uttered.

DON PEDRO: Amen, if you love her; for the lady is very well worthy.

CLAUDIO: That I love her, I feel.

DON PEDRO: That she is worthy, I know.

BENEDICK: That I neither feel how she should be loved nor know how she should be worthy, is the opinion that fire cannot melt out of me: I will die in it at the stake.

DON PEDRO: O Benedick, thou wast ever an obstinate heretic in the despite of beauty.

BENEDICK: I will do myself the right to trust none. I will live a bachelor.

DON PEDRO: I will see thee, ere I die, look pale with love.

BENEDICK: With anger, with sickness, or with hunger, my lord, not with love.

DON PEDRO: Well, as time shall try. "In time the savage bull doth bear the yoke." In the meantime, good Signior Benedick, repair to Leonato's; commend me to him, and tell him I will not fail him at supper.

MUSIC: *Light theme, in and under.*

NARRATOR: And so Don Pedro, on the behalf of his shy young friend, Claudio, speaks with Leonato about the young man's love for Hero, and gains Leonato's permission for Claudio to marry her. It is after dinner, and the assembled company consists of the young lovers, Claudio and Hero; her father, Leonato; the sharp-tongued Beatrice; and Don Pedro himself.

DON PEDRO: Here, Claudio, I have wooed in thy name, and fair Hero is won: I have broke with her father, and his good will obtained; name the day of marriage, and God give thee joy!

LEONATO: Count, take of me my daughter, and with her my fortunes: his Grace hath made the match, and all grace say Amen to it.

BEATRICE: Speak, Cousin Hero; or, if you cannot, stop his mouth with a kiss, and let him not speak neither.

HERO (*Embarrassed*): O cousin!

BEATRICE: Good Lord, for alliance! Thus goes everyone to the world but I, and I am sunburnt: I may sit in a corner and cry "Heigh-ho for a husband!"

DON PEDRO: Will you have me, lady?

BEATRICE: No, my lord—unless I might have another for

working days: your Grace is too costly to wear every day. But, I beseech your Grace, pardon me; I was born to speak all mirth and no matter.

LEONATO: Niece, will you look to those things I told you of?

BEATRICE (*Fading*): I cry you mercy, uncle. By your Grace's pardon.

DON PEDRO: By my troth, a pleasant-spirited lady.

LEONATO: My lord, she is never sad but when she sleeps, and not ever sad then; for I have heard my daughter say, she hath often dreamt of unhappiness, and waked herself with laughing.

HERO: So please you 'tis true.

CLAUDIO: She cannot endure to hear tell of a husband?

LEONATO: O, by no means; she mocks all her wooers out of suit.

DON PEDRO: She were an excellent wife for Benedick!

LEONATO (*Laughing*): O Lord, my lord, if they were but a week married, they would talk themselves mad!

DON PEDRO: Count Claudio, when mean you to go to church?

CLAUDIO: Tomorrow, my lord: time goes on crutches till love have all his rites.

LEONATO (*Protesting*): Not till Monday, my dear son, which is hence just seven-night; and a time too brief, too, to have all things answer my mind.

DON PEDRO: Come, Claudio, you shake the head at so long a breathing; but I warrant thee, the time shall not go dully by us. I will in the interim undertake one of Hercules' labors; which is, to bring Signior Benedick and the Lady Beatrice into a mountain of affection th' one with th' other. I would fain have it a match, and I doubt not but to fashion it, if you three will but minister such assistance as I shall give you direction.

LEONATO: My lord, I am for you, though it cost me ten nights' watchings.

CLAUDIO: And I, my lord.

DON PEDRO: And you, too, gentle Hero?

HERO: I will do any modest office, my lord, to help my cousin to a good husband.

DON PEDRO: And Benedick is not the unhopefullest husband that I know. Thus far can I praise him: he is of noble strain, of approved valor, and confirmed honesty. I will teach you how to humor your cousin, that she shall fall in love with Benedick; and I, with your two helps, will so practice on Benedick that, in despite of his quick wit and his queasy stomach, he shall fall in love with Beatrice. If we can do this, Cupid is no longer an archer. His glory shall be ours, for we are the only love-gods. Go in with me, and I will tell you my drift.

MUSIC: *Amusing theme, in and under.*

NARRATOR: The next afternoon, Don Pedro sees Benedick alone in an arbor. He arranges to walk past the arbor with Claudio and Leonato. The three plan to carry on a conversation that Benedick will overhear—all the time thinking himself unnoticed. Thus they plan to sow the seeds of love in the young Paduan's ear. In the arbor, Benedick is musing over the change that has come over Claudio since falling in love with Hero.

BENEDICK: I do much wonder that one man, seeing how much another man is a fool when he dedicates his behaviors to love, will, after he hath laughed at such shallow follies in others, become the argument of his own scorn by falling in love, and such a man is Claudio.

I will not be sworn but love may transform me to an oyster; but I'll take my oath on it, till he have made an oyster of me, he shall never make me such a fool. Till all graces be in one woman, one woman shall not come into my grace. Rich she shall be, that's certain; fair, or I'll never look on her; mild, or come not near me; of good discourse, an excellent musician, and her hair shall be of what colour—it please God. But soft! Here come the Prince, Signior Leonato and Monsieur Love! I will hide in the arbor.

DON PEDRO (*Fading on; the entire scene, however, except for Benedick, is played slightly off mike, with voices raised so he may overhear*): Come hither, Leonato. What was it you told me of today, that your niece Beatrice was in love with Signior Benedick?

CLAUDIO (*As an aside*): O, ay, stalk on, stalk on; the fowl sits. (*Aloud*) I did never think that lady would have loved any man.

LEONATO: No, nor I either; but most wonderful that she should so dote on Signior Benedick, whom she hath in all outward behaviors seemed ever to abhor!

BENEDICK (*To himself, in close*): Is't possible? Sits the wind in that corner?

LEONATO: By my troth, my lord, I cannot tell what to think of it but that she loves him with an enraged affection: it is past the infinite of thought.

DON PEDRO: Maybe she doth but counterfeit.

LEONATO: There was never counterfeit of passion came so near the life of passion as she discovers it.

CLAUDIO (*As an aside*): Bait the hook well; this fish will bite.

DON PEDRO: I would have thought her spirit had been invincible against all assaults of affection.

LEONATO: I would have sworn it had, my lord; especially against Benedick.

BENEDICK (*To himself*): I should think this a trick, but that the white-bearded fellow speaks it. Knavery cannot, sure, hide himself behind such reverence.

CLAUDIO: 'Tis true, indeed; so your daughter says. "Shall I," says she, "that have so oft encountered him with scorn, write to him that I love him?" Then down upon her knees she falls, weeps, sobs, beats her heart, tears her hair, prays, curses: "O sweet Benedick! God give me patience!"

DON PEDRO: It were good that Benedick knew of it by some other, if she will not discover it.

CLAUDIO: To what end? He would make but a sport of it and torment the poor lady worse.

DON PEDRO: She's an excellent sweet lady.

LEONATO: And she's exceeding wise.

DON PEDRO: In everything but in loving Benedick.

CLAUDIO: Never tell him, my lord: let her wear it out with good counsel.

LEONATO: Nay, that's impossible. She may wear her heart out first.

DON PEDRO: Well, we will hear further of it by your daughter; let it cool the while. I love Benedick well; and I could wish he would modestly examine himself, to see how much he is unworthy so good a lady.

LEONATO (*Fading*): My lord, will you walk? Dinner is ready.

BENEDICK (*Amazed*): This can be no trick; the conference

was sadly borne. They have the truth of this from Hero. Love me! Why, it must be requited! I hear how I am censured. I did never think to marry. I must not seem proud. Happy are they that hear their detractions and can put them to mending. They say the lady is fair; 'tis a truth, I can bear them witness. And wise, but not for loving me. I *will* be horribly in love with her! I may chance have some remnants of wit broken on me, because I have railed so long against marriage; but doth not the appetite alter? A man loves the meat in his youth that he cannot endure in his age. Shall quips and sentences awe a man from the career of his humor? No, the world must be peopled! When I said I would die a bachelor, I did not think I should live till I were married. But here comes Beatrice! By this day! She's a fair lady. I do spy some marks of love in her!

BEATRICE (*Fading on, coldly*): Against my will I am sent to bid you come to dinner.

BENEDICK (*Gently*): Fair Beatrice, I thank you for your pains.

BEATRICE: I took no more pains for those thanks than you take pains to thank me. If it had been painful, I would not have come.

BENEDICK: You take pleasure then in the message?

BEATRICE (*Fading*): Yea, just so much as you may take upon a knife's point and choke a daw withal. Fare you well.

BENEDICK: Ha! "Against my will I am sent to bid you come in to dinner." There's a double meaning in that! "I took no more pains for those thanks than you took pains to thank me"; that's as much as to say, "Any pains that I take for you is as easy as thanks." If I do not take pity on her, I am a villain. If I do not love her, I am an un-believer! I will go get her picture!

MUSIC: *Delightful theme, in and under.*

NARRATOR: The next step is to convince Beatrice that Benedick loves *her*. A similar plot is hatched between Hero and her serving woman, Ursula, who wait for Beatrice in the garden.

HERO: Now, Ursula, when Beatrice doth come,
Our talk must only be of Benedick.
When I do name him, let it be thy part
To praise him more than ever man did merit:
My talk to thee must be how Benedick
Is sick in love with Beatrice. Now begin:
For look where Beatrice, like a lapwing, runs
Close by the ground to hear our conference.

URSULA: Even now she's listening in the arbor!

HERO: Then go we near her, that her ear lose nothing
Of the false sweet bait that we lay for it.
(*Raising her voice*) No, truly, Ursula, she is too disdain-
ful.

URSULA: But are you sure that Benedick loves Beatrice?

HERO: So says the Prince and my new-trothed lord.

URSULA: And did they bid you tell her of it, madam?

HERO: They did entreat me to acquaint her of it;
But I persuaded them, if they lov'd Benedick,
To wish him wrestle with affection,
And never to let Beatrice know of it.

URSULA: Why did you so?

HERO: I know he doth deserve
As much as may be yielded to a man;
But Nature never fram'd a woman's heart

Of prouder stuff than that of Beatrice.
Disdain and scorn ride sparkling in her eyes!
URSULA: Sure, sure, such carping is not commendable.
HERO: No; not to be so odd and from all fashions
As Beatrice is, cannot be commendable.
But who dare tell her so? O, she would laugh!
Therefore let Benedick, like cover'd fire,
Consume away in sighs, waste inwardly.
No; rather I will go to Benedick
And counsel him to fight against his passion;
And, truly, I'll devise some honest slanders
To stain my cousin with: one doth not know
How much an ill word may empoison liking.
URSULA: O, do not do your cousin such a wrong.
She cannot be so much without true judgement
As to refuse the Signior Benedick.
Speaking my fancy, Signior Benedick,
For shape, for bearing, argument and valor,
Goes foremost in report through Italy.
HERO: Indeed, he hath an excellent good name!
URSULA (*In close, in confidence*): She's limed, I warrant
you! We have caught her, madam!
HERO (*Fading, softly*): If it proves so, then loving goes
by haps:
Some Cupid kills with arrows, some with traps!
Come; let's away!
BEATRICE (*Fading on, amazed*): What fire is in mine ears?
Can this be true?
Stand I condemn'd for pride and scorn so much?
Contempt, farewell! And maiden pride, adieu!
No glory lives behind the back of such.
And, Benedick, love on; I will requite thee,

Taming my wild heart to thy loving hand.
If thou dost love, my kindness shall incite thee
To bind our loves up in a holy band;
For others say thou dost deserve, and I
Believe it better than reportingly.

MUSIC: *Delightful theme, in and under.*

NARRATOR: Thus Benedick and Beatrice begin to love
each other. The following afternoon, as Claudio and
Don Pedro are strolling through the garden . . .

DON PEDRO: Look you, Claudio. Here is Benedick; from
the crown of his head to the sole of his foot, he is all
mirth: he hath twice or thrice cut Cupid's bowstring,
and the little hangman dare not shoot him. He hath a
heart as sound as a bell and his tongue is the clapper, for
what his heart thinks his tongue speaks.

BENEDICK (*Fading on*): Gallants, I am not as I have been.

DON PEDRO: So say I; methinks you are sadder.

CLAUDIO: I hope he be in love.

DON PEDRO: Hang him, truant! There's no true drop of
blood in him to be truly touched with love. If he be
sad, he wants money.

BENEDICK: I—I have the toothache.

DON PEDRO: What! Sigh for the toothache?

BENEDICK: Well, everyone can master a grief but he that
has it.

CLAUDIO: Yet say I, he is in love. If he be not in love with
some woman, there is no believing old signs. He brushes
his hat mornings; what should that bode?

DON PEDRO: Indeed, and he looks younger than he did,
by the loss of a beard.

CLAUDIO: That's as much as to say, the sweet youth's in
love.

DON PEDRO: The greatest note of it is his melancholy.

CLAUDIO: And when was he wont to wash his face?

DON PEDRO: Indeed, that tells a heavy tale for him: conclude, conclude, he is in love.

CLAUDIO: Nay, but I know who loves him.

DON PEDRO: That would I know too: I warrant, one that knows him not.

CLAUDIO: Yes, and his ill conditions; and, in despite of all, dies for him.

BENEDICK (*Angrily*): Yet is this no charm for the toothache. (*Fading*) I give you good day, my lords!

CLAUDIO *and* DON PEDRO: (*Laugh uproariously.*)

MUSIC: *Lively theme, in and under.*

NARRATOR: And in Hero's chamber. . . .

HERO: Good morrow, coz.

BEATRICE (*Sighing*): Good morrow, sweet Hero.

HERO: Why, how now? Do you speak in the sick tune?

BEATRICE: I am out of all other tune, methinks.

HERO (*Teasing*): Clap's into "Light O'Love"; that goes without a burden. Do you sing it, and I'll dance it.

BEATRICE: What mean you, trow?

HERO: Nothing, I; but God send everyone their heart's desire.

BEATRICE: By my troth, I am sick.

HERO: Get you some of this distilled Carduus Benedictus, and lay it to your heart; it is the only thing for a qualm.

BEATRICE: Benedictus? Why Benedictus? You have some moral in this Benedictus.

HERO: Moral! No, by my troth, I have no moral meaning; I meant, plain holy-thistle. You may think perchance that I think you are in love. Nay, I am not such a fool to think you are in love or that you will be in love or that you can be in love. Yet Benedick was such another, and now is he become a man. He swore he would never marry; and yet now, in despite of his heart, he eats his meat without grudging; and how you may be converted I know not, but methinks you look with your eyes as other women do.

BEATRICE (*Angrily*): What pace is this that thy tongue keeps?

HERO (*Laughing*): Not a false gallop!

MUSIC: *Gay theme, in and under.*

NARRATOR: At last a week passes, and Hero becomes Claudio's bride. In the church, immediately after their marriage, Benedick resolves to discover the truth about Beatrice's heart, and moved with the spirit of romance which fills the air, he indicates the veiled bridesmaids, and asks of the priest:

BENEDICK: Soft and fair, friar. Which is Beatrice?

BEATRICE (*Fading on from slightly off mike*): I answer to that name. What is your will?

BENEDICK: Do not you love me?

BEATRICE: Why . . . no; no more than reason.

BENEDICK: Why, then your uncle and the Prince and Claudio

Have been deceived. They swore you did.

BEATRICE: Do not you love me?

BENEDICK: Troth, no; no more than reason.

BEATRICE: Why then, my cousin and her lady, Ursula,

Are much deceiv'd, for they did swear you did.

BENEDICK: They swore that you were almost sick for me.

BEATRICE: They swore that you were well-nigh dead for me.

BENEDICK: 'Tis no matter. Then you do not love me?

BEATRICE: No truly, but in a friendly recompense.

LEONATO: Come, Beatrice, I am sure you love the gentleman.

CLAUDIO: And I'll be sworn upon't that he loves her;
For here's a paper written in his hand,
A halting sonnet of his own pure brain,
Fashion'd to Beatrice.

HERO: And here's another
Writ in my cousin's hand, stol'n from her pocket,
Containing her affection unto Benedick.

BENEDICK: A miracle! Here's our own hands against our hearts. Come, Beatrice, I will have thee; but, by this light, I take thee for pity.

BEATRICE: I would not deny you; but, by this good day, I yield upon great persuasion; and partly to save your life, for I was told you were in a consumption.

BENEDICK: Peace! I will stop your mouth!

SOUND: *Kiss.*

DON PEDRO (*Laughing*): How dost thou, Benedick, the married man?

BENEDICK: I'll tell thee what, Prince; a college of wit-crackers cannot flout me out of my humor. Dost thou think I care for a satire or an epigram? No; if a man will be beaten with brains, he shall wear nothing handsome about him. In brief, since I do purpose to marry, I will think nothing to any purpose that the world can say against it; and therefore never flout at me for what I have said against it, for man is a giddy thing, and this is my conclusion.

CLAUDIO: I had well hoped thou wouldst have denied Beatrice, that I might have cudgelled thee out of thy single life!

BENEDICK: Come, come, we are friends; let's have a dance ere we are married, that we may lighten our own hearts . . . and our wives' heels!

SOUND: *General laugh.*

MUSIC: *Delightful theme, full to finish.*

THE END

As You Like It

Characters

CELIA	ORLANDO
ROSALIND	DUKE SENIOR
LE BEAU	NARRATOR
DUKE FREDERICK	

NARRATOR: Of all of Shakespeare's comedies, none is as charming, as everlastingly alive as the Arcadian fantasy which mixes reality and make-believe with reckless abandon: the story of two lovers whose affection must stand the tests of banishment, disguise, misfortune, and buffoonery. Here is William Shakespeare's *As You Like It*.

MUSIC: *Delightful theme, in and under.*

NARRATOR: Frederick, a French duke, has banished his elder brother, the rightful duke, and taken over his dominions. The elder Duke is living out his banishment in the near-by forest of Arden; but his daughter, Rosalind, has remained at her Uncle Frederick's court as companion to her cousin Celia, Frederick's daughter. Though she dearly loves her cousin, Rosalind is often melancholy, thinking sadly of her father, the rightful duke, wondering what has become of him.

CELIA: I pray thee, Rosalind, sweet my coz, be merry.

ROSALIND: Dear Celia, I show more mirth than I am mistress of. Unless you could teach me to forget a banished father, you must not learn me how to remember any extraordinary pleasure.

CELIA: Herein I see thou lovest me not with the full weight that I love thee. If my uncle, thy banished father, had banished thy uncle, the duke my father, so thou hadst been still with me, I could have taught my love to take thy father for mine.

ROSALIND: Well, I will forget the condition of my estate, to rejoice in yours. But here comes one of your father's courtiers, Monsieur Le Beau.

CELIA: *Bon jour,* Monsieur Le Beau. What's the news?

LE BEAU (*Fading on*): Fair princess, you have lost much good sport.

CELIA: Sport! Of what color?

LE BEAU: Good wrestling. I will tell you the beginning; and if it please your ladyships, you may see the end, for the best is yet to do; and here, where you are, they are coming to perform it. Listen. There comes an old man and his three sons to the court. All three have wrestled with Charles, the Duke's wrestler, and one by one have had their ribs broken!

ROSALIND: Alas! But is there any else longs to feel this broken music in his sides? Is there yet another dotes upon rib-breaking? Shall we see this wrestling, cousin?

LE BEAU: You must, if you stay here; for here is the place appointed for the wrestling, and they are ready to perform it.

CELIA: Yonder, sure, they are coming. Let us now stay and see it.

MUSIC: *Fanfare.*

NARRATOR: The Duke, Frederick, enters, accompanied by the court wrestler, Charles, and a handsome youth, who is evidently the challenger.

FREDERICK: Come on. Since the youth will not be entreated, his own peril on his forwardness.

ROSALIND: Is yonder the man?

LE BEAU: Even he, madam.

CELIA: Alas! He is too young: yet he looks successfully.

FREDERICK: How now, daughter and cousin! Are you crept hither to see the wrestling?

ROSALIND: Ay, my liege, so please you give us leave.

FREDERICK: You will take little delight in it, I can tell you. In pity of the challenger's youth, I would fain dissuade him, but he will not be entreated. Speak to him, ladies; see if you can move him.

CELIA: Call him hither, good Monsieur Le Beau.

FREDERICK (*Fading*): Do so. I'll not be by.

LE BEAU (*Fading slightly*): Monsieur the challenger, the princess calls for you.

ORLANDO (*Fading on*): I attend them with all respect and duty.

ROSALIND: Young man, have you challenged Charles the wrestler?

ORLANDO: No, fair princess; he is the general challenger: I come but in, as others do, to try with him the strength of my youth.

CELIA: Young gentleman, your spirits are too bold for your years. You have seen cruel proof of this man's strength. We pray you, for your own sake, to embrace your own safety and give over this attempt.

ROSALIND: Do, young sir. Your reputation shall not there-

fore be misprised. We will make it our suit to the duke
that the wrestling might not go forward.

ORLANDO: I beseech you, punish me not with your hard
thoughts, wherein I confess me much guilty, to deny
so fair and excellent ladies anything. But let your fair
eyes and gentle wishes go with me to my trial.

ROSALIND: The little strength that I have, I would it
were with you.

CELIA: And mine, to eke out hers.

ROSALIND: Fare you well. Pray heaven I be deceived in
you!

CELIA: Your heart's desires be with you!

FREDERICK (*Calling from off mike*): Come, where is this
young gallant that is so desirous to lie with his mother
earth?

MUSIC: *Long fanfare.*

NARRATOR: And so Charles, the wrestler, and the young
stranger fight; and much to the company's surprise, it is
Charles that is thrown.

FREDERICK: How dost thou, Charles?

LE BEAU: He cannot speak, my lord.

FREDERICK: Bear him away. What is thy name, young man?

ORLANDO: Orlando, my liege; the youngest son of Sir
Rowland de Boys.

FREDERICK: I would thou hadst been son to some man else!
The world esteem'd thy father honorable,
But I did find him still mine enemy.
But fare thee well; thou art a gallant youth.
(*Fading*) I would thou hadst told me of another father.

CELIA: Were I my father, coz, would I do this?

ORLANDO: I am more proud to be Sir Rowland's son,

His youngest son; and would not change that calling
To be adopted heir to Frederick.

ROSALIND: My father lov'd Sir Rowland as his soul,
And all the world was of my father's mind.

CELIA: Gentle cousin,
Let us thank him and encourage him.

ROSALIND: Gentleman! Come hither, good Orlando.
Take this golden chain from 'round my neck.
Wear this for me, one out of suits with fortune,
That could give more, but that her hand lacks means.
Sir, you have wrestled well, and overthrown
More than your enemies.

CELIA: Will you go, coz?

ROSALIND (*Fading*): Have with you. Fare you well.

ORLANDO: What passion hangs these weights upon my
tongue?
I cannot speak to her, yet she urged conference.
O, poor Orlando, thou art overthrown!

LE BEAU (*Fading on, slightly*): Good sir, I do in friend-
ship counsel you
To leave this place. Albeit you have deserv'd
High commendation, true applause and love,
Yet such is now the duke's condition
That he misconstrues all that you have done.

ORLANDO: I thank you, sir; and pray you, tell me this;
Which of the two was daughter of the duke,
That here was at the wrestling?

LE BEAU: Neither his daughter, if we judge by manners:
But yet, indeed, the smaller is his daughter:
The other is daughter to the banished duke,
And here detain'd by her usurping uncle,

To keep his daughter, Celia, company.
And, on my life, his malice 'gainst the lady
Will suddenly break forth. Sir, fare you well.
Hereafter, in a better world than this,
I shall desire more love and knowledge of you.

ORLANDO: I rest much bounden to you. Fare you well.
Thus must I from the smoke into the smother.
But heavenly Rosalind!

MUSIC: *Delightful theme, in and under.*

NARRATOR: Thus, on the advice of Le Beau, Orlando decides to escape the anger of Duke Frederick, who is an
enemy to Orlando's father. And so the young man be-
takes himself to the near-by forest of Arden. As Le Beau
had suspected, Frederick is also about to vent his anger
upon Rosalind, the daughter of the banished Duke.
Rosalind has fallen in love with Orlando.

CELIA: Why, cousin! Why, Rosalind! Cupid have mercy!
Come, wrestle with thy affections.

ROSALIND: O, they take the part of a better wrestler than
myself.

CELIA: O, a good wish upon you! Is it possible, on such a
sudden, you should fall into so strong a liking with
young Orlando?

ROSALIND: The duke my father loved his father dearly.

CELIA: Doth it therefore ensue that you should love his
son dearly? By this kind of chase, I should hate him, for
my father hated his father dearly; yet I hate not Orlando.

ROSALIND: No, faith, hate him not for my sake. Look, here
comes the duke.

CELIA: With his eyes full of anger.

FREDERICK (*Fading on, coldly*): Mistress, dispatch you
with your safest haste,
And get you from our court.

ROSALIND: Me, uncle?

FREDERICK: You, cousin.
Within these ten days if that thou be'st found
So near our public court as twenty miles,
Thou diest for it.

ROSALIND: I do beseech your Grace,
Let me the knowledge of my fault bear with me.

FREDERICK: Let it suffice thee that I trust thee not.

ROSALIND: Yet your mistrust cannot make me a traitor.

FREDERICK: Thou art thy father's daughter; there's enough.

ROSALIND: So was I when your Highness took his duke-
dom;
So was I when your Highness banish'd him.
Treason is not inherited, my lord;
My father—aye, your brother—was no traitor.

CELIA: Dear sovereign, hear me speak.
If she be traitor, so am I. Be just!

FREDERICK: Firm and irrevocable is my doom,
Which I have pass'd upon her; she is banish'd.

CELIA: Pronounce that sentence then, on me, my liege:
I cannot live out of her company.

FREDERICK: You are a fool. You, niece, provide yourself.
If you outstay the time, upon my honor,
(*Fading*) And in the greatness of my word, you die.

CELIA: O my poor Rosalind! Whither wilt thou go?
Prithee, be cheerful. Know'st thou not, the duke
Hath banish'd me, his daughter?

ROSALIND: That he hath not.

CELIA: No, hath not? Rosalind lacks then the love
    Which teacheth thee that thou and I am one.
    Shall we be sunder'd? Shall we part, sweet girl?
    No; let my father seek another heir.
    Therefore devise with me how we may fly.
    Say what thou canst, I'll go along with thee.

ROSALIND: Why, whither shall we go?

CELIA: To seek my uncle in the forest of Arden.

ROSALIND: Alas, what danger will it be to us,
    Maids as we are, to travel forth so far!

CELIA: I'll put myself in poor and mean attire,
    And with a kind of umber smirch my face;
    The like do you. So shall we pass along
    And never stir assailants.

ROSALIND: Were it not better,
    Because that I am more than common tall,
    That I did suit me all points like a man?

CELIA: What shall I call thee when thou art a man?

ROSALIND: I'll have no worse a name than Jove's own
    page,
    And therefore look you call me Ganymede.
    But what will you be call'd?

CELIA: Something that hath a reference to my state:
    No longer Celia, but Aliena. Let's away,
    And get our jewels and our wealth together,
    Devise the fittest time and safest way
    To hide us from pursuit that will be made
    After my flight. Now go we in content
    To liberty and not to banishment.

MUSIC: *Light-hearted theme, in and under.*

NARRATOR: So, banished from her uncle's court, Rosalind
    disguises herself in the costume of a peasant man, and

takes the name Ganymede. Dressing herself in a ragged dress, Celia takes the name Aliena, and the two steal forth, and make their way to the forest of Arden. Having reached the forest ahead of them, Orlando spends his days writing poetry to Rosalind, with whom he is in love, hanging his ballads on branches, and carving her name into the barks of trees.

ORLANDO: Hang there, my verse, in witness of my love:
And thou, thrice-crowned queen of night, survey
With thy chaste eye, from thy pale sphere above,
Thy huntress' name, that my full life doth sway.
O Rosalind! These trees shall be my books,
And in their barks my thoughts I'll character,
That every eye, which in this forest looks,
Shall see thy virtue witness'd everywhere.
Run, run, Orlando: carve on every tree
The fair, the chaste, and unexpressive she.

MUSIC: *Romantic theme, in and under.*

NARRATOR: Upon reaching the forest of Arden, Rosalind and Celia—or, rather, Ganymede and Aliena, as they call themselves—buy a cottage and sheep, and pretend to be brother and sister. One day, walking through the wood, Rosalind, disguised as Ganymede, comes upon one of Orlando's verses, pinned to a tree.

ROSALIND (*Reading*): "From the east to western Ind,
No jewel is like Rosalind.
All the pictures fairest lined
Are but black to Rosalind.
Let no face be kept in mind,
But the fair of Rosalind."

What means this verse, I wonder? But, peace! Here comes my sister, reading. Stand aside!

CELIA (*Fading on, reading*): "Now upon the fairest
  boughs,
Or at every sentence end,
Will I Rosalinda write;
Teaching all that read to know
The quintessence of every sprite
Heaven would in little show."

ROSALIND: O most gentle pulpiter! What tedious homily
of love have you wearied your parishioners withal, and
never cried "Have patience, good people!"

CELIA: How now! Didst thou hear these verses?

ROSALIND: O yes, I heard them all.

CELIA: But didst thou hear without wondering, how thy
name should be hanged and carved upon these trees?

ROSALIND: I was seven of the nine days out of the wonder
before you came; for look here what I found on a
palm-tree; I was never so be-rimed!

CELIA: Trow you who hath done this?

ROSALIND: Is it a man?

CELIA: And a chain, that you once wore, about his neck.
Change you color?

ROSALIND: I prithee, who?

CELIA: O wonderful, wonderful, and most wonderful wonderful! And yet again wonderful! And after that, out
of all whooping!

ROSALIND: Good my complexion! Dost thou think, though
I am caparison'd like a man, I have a doublet and hose
in my disposition? I prithee, tell me who is it quickly,
and speak apace.

CELIA: It is young Orlando, that tripped up the wrestler's
heels and your heart both, in an instant.

ROSALIND: Nay, but the devil take mocking.

CELIA: I' faith, coz, 'tis he.

ROSALIND: Orlando?

CELIA: Orlando.

ROSALIND: Alas the day! What shall I do with my doublet and hose? What did he when thou sawest him? What said he? How looked he? Wherein went he? What makes he here? Did he ask for me? Where remains he? How parted he with thee, and when shalt thou see him again? Answer me in one word.

CELIA: You must borrow me Gargantua's mouth first: 'tis a word too great for any mouth of this age's size.

ROSALIND: But doth he know that I am in this forest and in man's apparel? Looks he as freshly as he did the day he wrestled?

CELIA: You bring me out. Soft! Comes he not here?

ROSALIND: 'Tis he! I will speak to him like a saucy lackey, since I am disguised as a youth, and under that habit play the knave with him. (*Aloud*) Do you hear, forester?

ORLANDO (*Fading on*): Very well. What would you?

ROSALIND: I pray you, what is't o'clock?

ORLANDO: You should ask me what time o' day; there's no clock in the forest.

ROSALIND: Then there is no true lover in the forest; else sighing every minute and groaning every hour would detect the lazy foot of Time as well as a clock.

ORLANDO: And why not the swift foot of time? Had not that been as proper?

ROSALIND: By no means, sir. Time travels in divers paces with divers persons.

ORLANDO: Where dwell you, pretty youth?

ROSALIND: With this shepherdess, my sister; here in the skirts of the forest, like fringe upon a petticoat.

ORLANDO: Your accent is something finer than you could purchase in so removed a dwelling.

ROSALIND: I have been told so of many; but indeed, an old religious uncle of mine taught me to speak, who was in his youth an inland man; one that knew courtship too well, for there he fell in love. I have heard him read many lectures against it; and I thank God, I am not a woman, to be touched with so many giddy offences as he hath generally taxed their whole sex withal.

ORLANDO: Can you remember any of the principal evils he laid to their charge?

ROSALIND: No, I will not cast away my physic but on those that are sick. There is a man haunts the forest, that abuses our young plants with carving "Rosalind" on their barks; hangs odes upon hawthorns and elegies on brambles; all, forsooth, deifying the name of Rosalind. If I could meet that fancy-monger, I would give him some good counsel, for he seems to have the quotidian of love upon him.

ORLANDO: I am he that is so love-shaked. I pray you, tell me your remedy.

ROSALIND: There is none of my uncle's marks upon you: he taught me how to know a man in love.

ORLANDO: What were his marks?

ROSALIND: A lean cheek, which you have not; a blue eye and sunken, which you have not. Your hose should be ungartered, your sleeve unbuttoned, and everything about you demonstrating a careless desolation. But you are no such man.

ORLANDO: Fair youth, I would I could make thee believe I love.

ROSALIND: Me believe it! You may as soon make her that you love believe it! But in good sooth, are you he that hangs the verses on the trees?

ORLANDO: I swear to thee, youth, by the white hand of Rosalind, I am that he, that unfortunate he!

ROSALIND: But are you so much in love as your rimes speak?

ORLANDO: Neither rime nor reason can express how much.

ROSALIND: Love is merely a madness, yet I profess curing it by counsel.

ORLANDO: Did you ever cure any so?

ROSALIND: Yes, one; and in this manner. He was to imagine me his love, his mistress; and I set him every day to woo me. At which time would I grieve, be effeminate, changeable, longing and liking, shallow, inconstant, full of tears, full of smiles, for every passion something, and for no passion truly anything. And thus I cured him.

ORLANDO: I would not be cured, youth.

ROSALIND: I would cure you, if you would but call me Rosalind, and come every day to my cote and woo me.

ORLANDO: Now, by the faith of my love, I will. Tell me where it is.

ROSALIND: Go with me to it and I'll show it you.

ORLANDO: With all my heart, good youth.

ROSALIND: Nay, you must call me Rosalind. Come sister, will you go?

MUSIC: *Delightful theme, in and under.*

NARRATOR: And so it is devised that Orlando, not knowing the true identity of Ganymede, shall make love to that youth as though he were Rosalind—which, of course, Ganymede truly is!

ORLANDO (*Fading on*): Good day and happiness, good Ganymede—

Or, rather, must I call you Rosalind.

ROSALIND: Why, how now, Orlando! Where have you been all this while? You a lover! An you serve me such another trick, never come in my sight more.

ORLANDO: My fair Rosalind, I come within an hour of my promise.

ROSALIND: Break an hour's promise in love!

ORLANDO: Pardon me, dear Rosalind.

ROSALIND: Come, woo me, woo me; for I am in a holiday humor. What would you say to me now, an I were your very very Rosalind?

ORLANDO: I would kiss before I spoke.

ROSALIND: Nay, you were better speak first, and when you were gravelled for lack of matter, you might take occasion to kiss.

ORLANDO: And if the kiss be denied?

ROSALIND: Then she puts you to entreaty, and there begins new matter.

ORLANDO: Who could be out, being before his beloved mistress?

ROSALIND: Am not I your Rosalind?

ORLANDO: I take some joy to say you are, because I would be talking of her.

ROSALIND: Well, in her person, I say I will not have you.

ORLANDO: I would not have my right Rosalind of this mind; for, I protest, her frown might kill me.

ROSALIND: By this hand, it will not kill a fly. But come, now. Ask me what you will, I will grant it.

ORLANDO: Then love me, Rosalind.

ROSALIND: Yes, faith will I, Fridays and Saturdays and all.

ORLANDO: And wilt thou have me?

ROSALIND: Ay, and twenty such.

ORLANDO: What sayest thou?

ROSALIND: Can one desire too much of a good thing?

ORLANDO: I take thee, Rosalind, for wife.

ROSALIND: I do take thee, Orlando, for my husband.

ORLANDO: But will my Rosalind do so?

ROSALIND: By my life, she will do as I do.

ORLANDO: O, but she is wise!

ROSALIND: Or else she could not have the wit to do this!

MUSIC: *Delightful theme, in and under.*

NARRATOR: Completely swept away, Rosalind confesses her deep devotion to her cousin Celia, who teases her.

CELIA: You have simply misused our sex in your love-prate. We must have your doublet and hose plucked over your head, and show the world what the bird hath done to her own nest.

ROSALIND: O coz, coz, coz, my pretty little coz, that thou didst know how many fathom deep I am in love! But it cannot be sounded. My affection hath an unknown bottom, like the bay of Portugal.

CELIA: Or rather, bottomless; that as fast as you pour affection in, it runs out.

ROSALIND: More in than out! How deep I am in love!

MUSIC: *Romantic theme, in and under.*

NARRATOR: At their next meeting, Orlando sadly tells the disguised Rosalind that on the morrow, two foresters are to be married in the presence of the banished Duke, with whom Orlando has been living in the wood. As sad as Orlando is to think of another's marrying while he must be without his love, so is Rosalind overjoyed to learn that her father is well, and is a friend to Orlando. And convinced of Orlando's love, she resolves to marry him, and as he tells her of the foresters' projected marriage, she devises a plan.

ORLANDO: They shall be married tomorrow, and I will bid the duke to the nuptial. But, O! How bitter a thing it is to look into happiness through another man's eyes.

ROSALIND: Why then, tomorrow I cannot serve your turn for Rosalind?

ORLANDO: I can live no longer by thinking.

ROSALIND: I will weary you no longer with idle talking. Know of me, then, I have, since I was three years old, conversed with a magician most profound in his art. If you do love Rosalind so near the heart as your gesture cries it out, when these rustics wed each other, you shall marry her. I know into what straits of fortune she is driven; and it is not impossible to me, if appear not inconvenient to you, to set her before your eyes tomorrow, human as she is, and without any danger.

ORLANDO: Speakest thou in sober meanings?

ROSALIND: By my life, I do; which I tender dearly, though I say I am a magician. Therefore, put you in your best array; bid your friends; for if you will be married tomorrow, you shall; and to Rosalind, if you will. I will satisfy you, if ever I satisfy man, and you shall be married tomorrow.

MUSIC: *Delightful theme, in and under.*

NARRATOR: The next afternoon, Orlando meets at the appointed place with the banished Duke Senior, Rosalind's father, to wait the coming of Ganymede.

DUKE SENIOR: Dost thou believe, Orlando, that the boy
Can do all this that he hath promised?

ORLANDO: I sometimes do believe, and sometimes do not;
As those that fear—they hope, and know they fear.

ROSALIND (*Fading on*): Patience once more, whiles our
compact is urg'd.
You say, if I bring in your Rosalind,
You will bestow her on Orlando here?

DUKE SENIOR: That would I, had I kingdoms to give with
her.

ROSALIND: And you say, you will have her when I bring
her?

ORLANDO: That would I, were I of all kingdoms king.

ROSALIND: I have promis'd to make all this matter even.
Keep your word, O duke, to give your daughter;
(*Fading*) You yours, Orlando, to receive his daughter.

DUKE SENIOR: I do remember in this shepherd boy
Some lively touches of my daughter's favor.

ORLANDO: My lord, the first time that I ever saw him,
Methought he was a brother to your daughter;
But, my good lord, this boy is forest-born,
And hath been tutor'd in the rudiments
Of many desperate studies by his uncle,
Whom he reports to be a great magician,
Obscured in the circle of this forest.

DUKE (*In wonder*): But soft, Orlando! See what ladies
come!

NARRATOR: To the amazement of the Duke and Orlando,
Rosalind and Celia, having thrown off their disguises,
come forward to them through the trees, dressed as the
royal princesses they are.

ROSALIND (*Fading on*): To you I give myself, for I am
yours, Father.
To you I give myself, for I am yours, husband.

DUKE SENIOR: If there be truth in sight, you are my daughter.

ORLANDO: If there be truth in sight, you are my Rosalind.

ROSALIND: I'll have no father, if you be not he.
I'll have no husband, if you be not he.

CELIA: Will none speak welcome to a humble niece?

DUKE SENIOR: O my dear niece! Welcome thou art to me.
Even daughter, welcome in no less degree!

MUSIC: *Romantic theme, sneak into background under following.*

DUKE SENIOR: Proceed, proceed! We will begin these rites,
As we do trust they'll end . . . in true delights¹

MUSIC: *Full to finish.*

THE END

The Tempest

Characters

MIRANDA
PROSPERO
ARIEL
FERDINAND
CALIBAN

GONZALO
ALONSO, *King of Naples*
SEBASTIAN
ANTONIO
NARRATOR

NARRATOR: Long before the advent of radio, television and the public library, William Shakespeare took a turn at writing a play which, today, would be classified as Science Fiction. Filled with sorcery, spirits and secret arts, here is the Bard of Avon's wonderful and magical *The Tempest*.

SOUND: *Crack of lightning and peal of thunder.*

MUSIC: *Mysterious theme, in and under.*

NARRATOR: The scene is a rockbound island, far at sea. As the play begins, a great tempest is raging, setting the ocean waters surrounding the island into furious action. The storm has been brought about by the magician, Prospero, in order to wreck a ship that is traveling near by, on which sail several men who at one time had done Prospero great wrong. Prospero's beautiful young

daughter, Miranda, is terrified as she watches the ship-
wreck, for she does not know that her father intends to
save the lives of all aboard. In terror for the sailors'
lives, she pleads with her father to stop the tempest.

MIRANDA (*A sweet young voice*): If by your art, my dearest
　　father, you have
　　Put the wild waters in this roar, allay them.
　　Let the tempest stop! O, I have suffered
　　With those that I saw suffer! A brave vessel,
　　Who had, no doubt, some noble creatures on her,
　　Dash'd all to pieces.

PROSPERO (*A majestic old man*): Be collected;
　　No more amazement. Tell your piteous heart
　　There's no harm done.

MIRANDA: O, woe the day!

PROSPERO: No harm!
　　I have done nothing but in care of thee,
　　Of thee, my dear one, thee my daughter, who
　　Art ignorant of what thou art, naught knowing
　　Of whence I am, nor that I am more better
　　Than Prospero, master of a full poor cell,
　　And thy no greater father.

MIRANDA: More to know
　　Did never meddle with my thoughts.

PROSPERO: 'Tis time
　　I should inform thee farther. Lend thy hand;
　　Obey and be attentive. Canst thou remember
　　A time before we came unto this cell?
　　I do not think thou canst, for then thou wast not
　　Out three years old.

MIRANDA: Certainly, sir, I can.

'Tis far off, and rather like a dream.

Had I not women once that tended me?

PROSPERO: Thou hadst, and more, Miranda. Listen close,

And I shall tell thee who we rightly are.

(*Fading*) Twelve years since, Miranda, twelve years since,

Thy father was the Duke of Milan.

MUSIC: *In and under.*

NARRATOR: And so, after twelve years, Miranda learns of her noble birth. Prospero tells her that he had been the Duke of Milan. As he was much interested in magic, Prospero had devoted all his time to study, and gradually the affairs of state drifted into the hands of his villainous brother, Antonio. Once Antonio achieved power, he conspired with Alonso, King of Naples, and the two set Prospero and Miranda, who was then a child, adrift in a leaky boat. A loyal servant, however—one Gonzalo—stocked the boat with provisions and Prospero's magic books, and so instead of drowning, the two drifted to an uninhabited island, where for twelve years they have lived. During those years, Prospero has developed his magic powers, and tamed as his servants two creatures that he found on the island; Ariel, the good spirit, and Caliban, a savage and stupid slave.

PROSPERO (*Fading on*): And thus, my child, your history is done.

MIRANDA: Heavens thank you for't! And now, I pray you, sir,

For still 'tis beating in my mind, your reason

For raising this sea-storm?

PROSPERO: Know thus far forth.

By accident most strange, bountiful Fortune,

Hath those very enemies I spoke of,
Antonio, and Alonso, King of Naples,
Sebastian, that king's most villainous brother,
In company with the faithful old Gonzalo,
And Ferdinand, Alonso's only son,
Brought to this shore. Ariel's with them now.
But, thou art inclined to sleep; 'tis a good dullness,
And give it way. I know thou canst not choose.

MUSIC: *Mysterious but gentle theme, in and under.*

PROSPERO: Come, my faithful servant, Ariel!
Come and do your master Prospero's will!

ARIEL (*A delicate voice, fading on*): All hail, great master!
Grave sir, hail! I come,
To answer thy best pleasure, be't to fly,
To swim, to dive into the fire, to ride
On the curl'd clouds. To thy strong bidding task
Ariel and all his quality.

PROSPERO: Hast thou, spirit,
Perform'd to point the tempest that I bade thee?

ARIEL: To every article.
I boarded the king's ship; now on the beak,
Now in the waist, the deck, in every cabin,
I flam'd amazement. Sometime I'd divide,
And burn in many places: on the topmast,
The yards and bowsprit, would I flame distinctly,
Then meet and join.

PROSPERO: My brave spirit!
Who was so firm, so constant, that this coil
Would not affect his reason?

ARIEL: Not a soul but felt a fever of the mad,
Plung'd in the foaming brine and quit the vessel;
The King's son, Ferdinand, was the first that leap'd.

PROSPERO: Why, that's my spirit! Was not this nigh shore?

ARIEL: Not a hair perished!
    On their sustaining garments not a blemish,
    But fresher than before; and as thou bad'st me,
    In troops I have dispers'd them 'bout the isle.
    The King's son I have landed by himself,
    Whom I left cooling of the air with sighs.
    And all the ships are safely in the bay!

PROSPERO: Ariel, thy charge
    Exactly is perform'd; but there's more work.
    Go make thyself like a nymph o' the sea; be subject
    To no sight but thine and mine, invisible
    To every eyeball else. Go take this shape,
    And with accompaniment of magic music,
    Lure thou the princely Ferdinand to me.

ARIEL (*Fading*): I go, my master!

MUSIC: *Enchanted theme, in and under.*

NARRATOR: As Ariel has separated the survivors into
    groups about the island, each thinks that all the others
    are drowned. Doing his master's bidding, Ariel makes
    himself invisible, and with magic music, lures the hand-
    some Prince Ferdinand to Prospero's cave. While won-
    dering where the music originates, Ferdinand also
    thinks with melancholy on the supposed death of his
    father, the King of Naples.

MUSIC: *Up slightly, then under following scene.*

FERDINAND (*A young, manly voice*): Where should this
    music be? I' th' air or th' earth?
    It sounds no more; and sure, it waits upon
    Some god o' the island. Sitting on a bank,
    Weeping again the King my father's wreck,
    This music crept by me upon the waters,

Allaying both their fury and my passion

With its sweet air; thence I have followed it,

Or it hath drawn me rather.

(*Fading*) The ditty does remember my drown'd father.

PROSPERO (*Fading on*): The fring'd curtains of thine eyes advance,

Miranda, daughter. Say what thou seest yond.

MIRANDA (*Wondering*): What is yon creature, father? Is't a spirit?

PROSPERO: No, wench; it eats and sleeps and hath such senses

As we have, such. This gallant which thou seest

Was in the wreck; and, but he's something stain'd

With grief, that's beauty's canker, thou mightst call him

A goodly person. He hath lost his fellows

And strays about to find 'em.

MIRANDA: I might call him

A thing divine; for nothing natural

I ever saw so noble.

FERDINAND (*Fading on*): Most sure, the goddess

On whom these airs attend! Vouchsafe my prayer

May know if you remain upon this island,

How I may bear me here: O you wonder!

MIRANDA (*With a light laugh*): No wonder, sir. I am a living maid.

FERDINAND (*Overjoyed*): My language! Heavens!

I am the best of them that speak this speech,

Were I but where 'tis spoken.

PROSPERO (*Feigning anger*): How? The best?

What wert thou, if the King of Naples heard thee?

FERDINAND: A single thing, as I am now, that wonders

To hear thee speak of Naples. Myself am Naples,
Who with mine eyes, never since at ebb, beheld
The King my father wreck'd.

MIRANDA (*Tenderly*): Alack, for mercy!

PROSPERO (*As an aside*): They are both in either's powers;
but this swift business,
I must uneasy make, lest too light winning
Make the prize light. (*Aloud*) One word more; I charge
thee
That thou attend me. Thou dost here usurp
The name thou owest not; and hast put thyself
Upon this island as a spy, to win it
From me, the lord on't.

FERDINAND: No, as I am a man!

MIRANDA: Pity, move my father!

PROSPERO: Speak not you for him, Miranda; he's a traitor.
Come, sirrah, to my cave. Thou art my prisoner!

FERDINAND: Might I but through my prison once a day
Behold this maid, all corners else o' th' earth
Let liberty make use of; space enough
Have I in such a prison.

MIRANDA: Be of comfort.
My father's of a better nature, sir,
Than he appears by speech. This is unwonted
Which now came from him.

PROSPERO (*Fading*): Speak not for him, Miranda. Come!
Follow!

MUSIC: *Delightful theme, in and under.*

NARRATOR: Not only does Prospero wield control over the
humans on the island, and over Ariel, the good-hearted
sprite, but his powers extend also to include Caliban, a

lowly, foul beast—evil-hearted and ignorant. Kept as a slave by Prospero, Caliban continually hurls his wrath at the magician, and constantly bemoans his fate.

CALIBAN: All the infections that the sun sucks up
From bogs, fens, flats, on Prospero fall, and make him
By inch-meal a disease! His spirits hear me,
And yet I needs must curse. If he should bid 'em,
For every trifle are they set upon me;
Sometimes like apes, that mow and chatter at me,
And after bite me; then like hedgehogs, which
Lie tumbling in my barefoot way. And now
He'll send a spirit out to torment me
If I perform my weary tasks too slowly.
Let all my curses down on Prospero fall!

MUSIC: *In and under.*

NARRATOR: Despite these harmless threats of Caliban, Prospero's plans go well. For Miranda and Ferdinand, love for each other has come at once, and though he is secretly pleased, Prospero pretends to be angry with the young prince, forcing him to work as a servant. Elsewhere on the island, the King of Naples, Alonso, thinks his son Ferdinand is drowned; and faithful old Gonzalo, the servant who had many years before helped Prospero to escape, is trying to cheer him up.

GONZALO (*An elderly, kindly man*): Beseech you, sir, be merry; you have cause,
So have we all, of joy; for our escape
Is much beyond our loss. For, good sir, weigh
Our sorrow with our comfort.

ALONSO (*Middle-aged; despondently*): Prithee, peace.
You cram these words into mine ears against
The stomach of my sense. O thou mine heir

Of Naples and Milan, what strange fish
Hath made his meal on thee?

GONZALO: Sir, he may live;
I saw him beat the surges under him,
And ride upon their backs.

ALONSO (*Weeping miserably*): No, no, he's gone!

MUSIC: *Melancholy theme, in and under.*

NARRATOR: At Prospero's command, Ariel lulls the weeping King of Naples and good Gonzalo to sleep with
magic music. As they sleep, Sebastian, villainous brother
of the King, and Antonio, the usurping Duke of Milan,
come upon them, and seeing an opportunity to gain
greater fortunes, plot their murder. Prospero sees all
that happens on the island, however, and plans to send
Ariel and the magic music to the rescue of the sleepers
at the proper moment. The villains, Sebastian and Antonio, approach the sleeping King and servant.

SEBASTIAN: What a strange drowsiness possesses them!

ANTONIO: It is the quality o' the climate.

SEBASTIAN: Why doth it not then our eyelids sink? I find
not
Myself dispos'd to sleep.

ANTONIO: Nor I; my spirits are nimble.
How soundly do they sleep. But soft! What might,
Worthy Sebastian, O, what might—? No more:—
And yet, methinks I see it in thy face,
What thou shouldst be: the occasion speaks thee, and
My strong imagination sees a crown
Dropping upon thy head.

SEBASTIAN: What, art thou waking?

ANTONIO: Do you not hear me speak?

SEBASTIAN: I do; and surely it is out of thy sleep!

ANTONIO: Noble Sebastian,
    Thou let'st thy fortune sleep—die, rather; wink'st
    Whiles thou art waking. Will you grant with me
    That Ferdinand is drown'd?
SEBASTIAN: He's gone.
ANTONIO: Then tell me,
    Who's the next heir of Naples? O, that you bore
    The mind that I do! What a sleep were this
    For your advancement! Do you understand me?
SEBASTIAN (*Slowly*): Methinks I do.
ANTONIO: And how does your content
    Tender your own good fortune?
SEBASTIAN: I remember
    You did supplant your brother Prospero.
ANTONIO: True.
    And look how well my garments sit upon me;
    Much feater than before. My brother's servants
    Were then my fellows; now they are my men.
SEBASTIAN: But for your conscience?
ANTONIO: Ay, sir, where lies that? Twenty consciences
    That stand 'twixt me and Milan, candied be they
    And melt ere they molest! Here lies your brother,
    No better than the earth he lies upon
    If he were that which now he's like, that's dead;
    Whom I, with this obedient steel, three inches of it,
    Can lay to bed for ever.
SEBASTIAN: Thy case, dear friend,
    Shall be my precedent; as thou got'st Milan,
    I'll come by Naples. Draw thy sword. One stroke
    Shall free thee from the tribute which thou payest,
    And I the King shall love thee.

ANTONIO: Draw together;
  And when I rear my hand, do you the like
  To fall it on Gonzalo.

SOUND: *Swords being unsheathed.*

ANTONIO: Now let us both be sudden!

MUSIC: *Quivering chord, loud and sustained.*

ARIEL (*As an alarm*): Awake! Awake!

GONZALO (*In amazement and fright*): Now, good angels,
  preserve the King!

ALONSO (*Waking*): Why, how now? Ho, awake! Why are
  you drawn?

  Wherefore this ghastly looking, Antonio, Sebastian?

GONZALO: Put up your swords, and tell us what's the matter!

SEBASTIAN (*Stammering*): Whiles we stood here securing
  your repose,

  Even now, we heard a hollow burst of bellowing
  Like bulls, or rather lions. Did't not wake you?

ALONSO: I heard nothing.

ANTONIO: O, 'twas a din to fright a monster's ear,
  It was the roar of a whole herd of lions!

ALONSO: Heard you this, Gonzalo?

GONZALO: Upon mine honor, sir, I heard a humming,
  And that a strange one too, which did awake me.
  I shak'd you, sir, and cried: as mine eyes opened,
  I saw their weapons drawn: there was a noise,
  That's verily. 'Tis best we stand upon our guard,
  Or that we quit this place. Let's draw our weapons.

ALONSO: Lead off this ground; and let's make further
  search
  For my poor son.

GONZALO: Heavens keep him from these beasts!
 For he is, sure, i' the island!
ALONSO (*Fading*): Lead away.
ARIEL (*In close*): Prospero my lord shall know what I have
  done.
 So, King, go safely on to seek thy son.
MUSIC: *Mysterious theme, in and under.*
NARRATOR: Thus were the King of Naples and the faithful
  Gonzalo saved from death at the hands of Antonio and
  Sebastian by the intervention of Prospero's magic. Mean-
  while, to make Ferdinand prove his good faith, Prospero
  has set him the monstrous task of piling thousands of
  heavy logs in a great heap. Though his burden be heavy,
  however, Ferdinand's task is lightened by the thought
  of fair Miranda.
FERDINAND: There be some sports are painful, and their
   labor
 Delight in them sets off; some kinds of baseness
 Are nobly undergone, and most poor matters
 Point to rich ends. This my mean task
 Would be as heavy to me as odious, but
 This mistress which I serve quickens what's dead
 And makes my labors pleasures. O, she is
 Ten times more gentle than her father's crabbed,
 And he's compos'd of harshness. I must remove
 Some thousands of these logs and pile them up,
 Upon a sore injunction. My sweet mistress
 Weeps when she sees my work, and says such baseness
 Had never like executor. I forget;
 But these sweet thoughts do even refresh my labors,
 Most busiest when I do it.
MIRANDA (*Fading on*): Alas, now, pray you,

Work not so hard. I would the lightning had
Burnt up those logs that you are enjoin'd to pile!
Pray, set it down and rest you.
FERDINAND: O most dear mistress,
    The sun will set before I shall discharge
    What I must strive to do.
MIRANDA: If you'll sit down, I'll bear your logs the while.
FERDINAND: No, precious creature;
    I had rather crack my sinews, break my back,
    Than you should such dishonor undergo.
MIRANDA: It would become me. You look wearily.
FERDINAND: No, noble mistress; 'tis fresh morning with
    me
    When you are by at night. I do beseech you,
    What is your name?
MIRANDA: Miranda.
FERDINAND: Admir'd Miranda!
    Indeed, the top of admiration! You,
    So perfect and so peerless, are created
    Of every creature's best!
MIRANDA: Do you love me?
FERDINAND: O heaven, O earth, bear witness to this sound,
    And crown what I profess with kind event.
    I beyond all limit of what else i' th' world
    Do love, prize, honor you.
MIRANDA (*Crying gently*): I am a fool
    To weep at what I am glad of. But this is trifling!
    I am your wife, if you will marry me;
    If not, I'll die your maid. To be your fellow
    You may deny me; but I'll be your servant,
    Whether you will or no.

FERDINAND: My mistress, dearest;
And I thus humble ever.

MIRANDA: My husband then?

FERDINAND: Ay, with a heart as willing
As bondage e'er of freedom: here's my hand.

MIRANDA: And mine, with my heart in't; (*Fading*) And now farewell
Till half an hour hence.

FERDINAND (*Fading*): A thousand thousand!

PROSPERO (*Laughing, in close*): So glad of this as they I cannot be,
Who are surprised withal; but my rejoicing
At nothing can be more. I'll to my book
For yet ere supper-time must I perform
Much business appertaining.

MUSIC: *Romantic theme, in and under.*

NARRATOR: And so, Ferdinand and Miranda pledge their love for one another. With a happy heart, Prospero releases Ferdinand from his task, and gives the young lovers his blessings.

PROSPERO: If I have too austerely punish'd you,
Your compensation makes amends, for I
Have given you here a third of mine own life,
Or that for which I live who once again
I tender to thy hand. All thy vexations
Were but my trials of thy love, and thou
Hast strangely stood the test. Here, afore Heaven,
I ratify this my rich gift. O Ferdinand,
Do not smile at me that I boast her off,
For thou shalt find she will outstrip all praise
And make it halt behind her.

FERDINAND: I do believe it against an oracle.

PROSPERO: Then, as my gift and thine own acquisition
  Worthily purchas'd, take my daughter.
FERDINAND *and* MIRANDA (*Fading*): We wish you peace.
PROSPERO: What, Ariel! My industrious servant, Ariel!
ARIEL (*Fading on*): What would my potent master? Here
  I am.
PROSPERO: Say, my spirit,
  How fares the King and 's followers?
ARIEL: Confin'd together
  In the same fashion as you gave in charge,
  Just as you left them; all prisoners, sir,
  They cannot budge till your release. The King,
  His brother, and yours, abide all three distracted.
  For good Lord Gonzalo, tears run down his beard.
  If you now beheld them, your affections
  Would become tender.
PROSPERO: Dost thou think so, spirit?
ARIEL: Mine would, sir, were I human.
PROSPERO: And mine shall. Go, release them, Ariel.
  My charms I'll break, their senses I'll restore,
  And they shall be themselves.
ARIEL: I'll fetch them, sir.
MUSIC: *In and under.*
NARRATOR: While Ariel, still invisible, leads the ship-
  wrecked passengers to the clearing before Prospero's
  cave, the magician himself changes into the clothes
  which he wore as Duke of Milan, twelve years earlier,
  and prepares to greet the confused and wondering
  travelers.
GONZALO (*Fading on*): All torment, trouble, wonder and
  amazement

Inhabits here. Some heavenly power guide us!
But soft! What man is this?

PROSPERO: Behold, sir King,
The wronged Duke of Milan, Prospero!
For more assurance that a living Prince
Does now speak to thee, I embrace thy body;
And to thee and thy company I bid
A hearty welcome.

ALONSO (*Amazed*): Thy pulse, O Prospero, beats as of
flesh and blood.
Th' affliction of my mind amends, with which,
I fear, a madness held me: this must crave,
An if this be at all, a most strange story.
Thy dukedom I resign and do entreat
Thou pardon me my wrongs. But how should Prospero
Be living and be here?

PROSPERO: First, noble friend,
Let me embrace thine age, whose honor cannot
Be measur'd or confin'd.

GONZALO: Whether this be or be not, I'll not swear.

PROSPERO: You do yet taste
Some subtleties o' the isle, that will not let you
Believe things certain. Welcome, my friends, all.
But you, Antonio and Sebastian, were I so minded,
I here could pluck his Highness' frown upon you
And justify you traitors. At this time
I will tell no tales.

SEBASTIAN: The devil speaks in him!

PROSPERO: No. For you, most wicked Antonio, whom to
call brother
Would even infect my mouth, I do forgive

Thy rankest fault; all of them; and require
My dukedom of thee, which perforce, I know,
Thou must restore.

ALONSO: If thou be'st Prospero,
Give us particulars of thy preservation,
How thou hast met us here, whom three hours since
Were wreck'd upon this shore, where I have lost
My dear son Ferdinand. Irreparable loss!
And Patience says it is past her cure.

PROSPERO: I think
You have not sought her help, of whose soft grace
For the like loss I have her sovereign aid,
And rest myself content.

ALONSO: You the like loss!

PROSPERO: As great to me, for I have lost a daughter.

ALONSO: A daughter?
O heavens, that they were living both in Naples,
The King and Queen there! When did you lose your
   daughter?

PROSPERO: In this last tempest. Know you all for certain
That I am Prospero, and that very duke
Which was thrust forth of Milan, who most strangely
Upon this shore, where you were wreck'd, was landed,
To be lord on't. Welcome, Alonso.
This cave's my court. Here I have few attendants,
And subjects none abroad. Pray you, look in!

ALONSO (*Overjoyed*): 'Tis my son, Ferdinand! If this
   prove
A vision of the island, one dear son
Shall I twice lose.

SEBASTIAN: A most high miracle!

FERDINAND (*Fading on*): Though the seas threaten, they
     are merciful.

     I have curs'd them without cause.

ALONSO: Now all the blessings

     Of a glad father compass thee about!

MIRANDA (*Fading on*): O, wonder!

     How many goodly creatures are there here!

     How beauteous mankind is! O brave new world,

     That has such people in't!

ALONSO: Who is this maid?

FERDINAND: Sir, she is mortal—though more like a god-
     dess.

     I chose her when I could not ask my father

     For his advice, nor thought I had one. She

     Is daughter to this famous Duke of Milan.

     This lady makes him second father to me.

ALONSO: Then I am hers.

     But, O, how oddly will it sound that I

     Must ask my child's forgiveness.

PROSPERO: There, sir, stop.

     Let us not burden our remembrances with

     A heaviness that's gone.

GONZALO: Look down, you gods,

     And on this couple drop a blessed crown.

ALONSO: I say, Amen, Gonzalo.

PROSPERO: Sir, I invite your Highness and your train

     To my poor cell, where you shall take your rest

     For this one night; which, part of it, I'll waste

     With such discourse as, I not doubt, shall make it

     Go quick away—the story of my life

     And the particular accidents gone by

     Since I came to this isle. And in the morn

I'll bring you to your ship and so to Naples,
Where I have hope to see the nuptial
Of these our dear-belov'd solemnized:
And thence retire me to my Milan, where
Every third thought shall be my grave.
I promise you calm seas, auspicious gales,
And sail so expeditious that shall catch
Your royal fleet far off. My Ariel, chick,
That is thy charge. Then to the elements
Be free, and fare thou well. Please you draw near.
Music: *Happy theme, full to finish.*

THE END

Romeo and Juliet

Characters

PRINCE ESCALUS	JULIET
A SERVANT	HER NURSE
ROMEO	FRIAR LAURENCE
MERCUTIO	BALTHASAR
LORD CAPULET	MONTAGUE
TYBALT	NARRATOR

NARRATOR: Against the colorful life of fifteenth century Verona, William Shakespeare unfolded the greatest love story of all time. In an age of passionate pride and family feuds, there lived two noble houses, both wealthy, both cultured—the Capulets and the Montagues. Alike in many things, these two great families were mortal enemies. Not a week went by but the peace of fair Verona was disturbed by fighting among men of both houses—each determined to prove the superiority of his own family. Yet, from these opposed families came two star-crossed lovers—she a Capulet, and he a Montague. And against the clash of family pride, the tragic romance was enacted of this unhappy pair—Romeo and Juliet.

SOUND: *Turmoil of an angry crowd. Then, fanfare. Crowd subsides.*

PRINCE *(Angrily)*: Rebellious subjects, enemies to peace,
Profaners of this neighbor-stained steel,
Throw your mistempered weapons to the ground,
And hear the sentence of your moved prince.
Three civil brawls, bred of an airy word,
By thee, old Capulet, and Montague,
Have thrice disturbed the quiet of our streets.
If ever you disturb our streets again,
Your lives shall pay the forfeit of the peace.
For this time, all the rest depart away.
Once more, on pain of death, all men depart!

MUSIC: *Dramatic theme, in and under.*

NARRATOR: In an attempt to soothe his angered household, which is roused by the judgment imposed by the Prince of Verona, old Capulet plans a masquerade ball, and sends his servant, Peter, through the streets, with a list of those who are to be invited.

SERVANT *(Fading on)*: My master, Lord Capulet, has given me this list of names, and orders me to visit all whose names are written here. But how am I to find whose names are here writ? I cannot read! I must to the learned! Ah, here come two gentlemen; I shall ask them. I pray, sir, can you read?

ROMEO *(Fading on, pleasantly)*: Aye, if I know the letters and the language.

SERVANT: Pray thee, then, sir: read this list for me.

ROMEO: Why, 'tis a list of names that here are writ. "Signior Martino and his wife and daughters; County Anselme and his beauteous sisters; the lady widow of Vitruvio; Mercutio and his brother Valentine; mine uncle Capulet, his wife and daughters; my fair niece Rosaline; Signior Valentio and his cousin Tybalt." A fair assembly; whither should they come?

SERVANT: Up. To supper; at our house.

ROMEO: Whose house?

SERVANT: My master's. Now I'll tell you without asking: my master is the great rich Capulet; and if you be not of the house of Montague, I pray, come and crush a cup of wine. (*Fading*) Rest you merry, gentlemen!

ROMEO: Didst hear, Mercutio? A feast tonight,
Given by my old foe, Lord Capulet!

MERCUTIO: Aye, Romeo, I did mark the fellow well.
Let us proceed to feast at Capulet's.
Though we be Montagues, his ancient foes,
We'll hide our faces with the aid of masks,
And feast away the night in merriment.

ROMEO: Aye, good Mercutio. To Capulet's!

MUSIC: *Delightful theme, in and under.*

NARRATOR: And so Romeo and Mercutio, although of the enemy house of Montague, don costumes and masks, and go to the ball at rich Lord Capulet's.

CAPULET: Welcome, gentlemen! Welcome to my house!
Come, musicians, play. A hall! Give room!
Come, gentlemen and ladies. Come and dance!

MUSIC: *A pavanne.*

CAPULET: What ho, Tybalt!

TYBALT (*Angrily*): Uncle Capulet.

CAPULET: Why, how now, kinsman? Wherefore storm you so?

TYBALT: Uncle, see yon gentleman that wears a mask?
He that dances with your daughter, Juliet?

Uncle, that is a Montague, our foe;

A villain that is hither come to spite.

That villain Romeo has come to scorn!

CAPULET *(Pacifying him)*: Content thee, gentle coz, let him alone.

He bears him like a portly gentleman;

And, to say truth, Verona brags of him

To be a virtuous and well-govern'd youth.

Show a fair presence and put off these frowns,

An ill-beseeming semblance for a feast.

TYBALT: It fits, when such a villain is a guest.

CAPULET: Tybalt! I tell thee, he shall be endured!

Am I the master here, or you? Go to.

TYBALT: Patience perforce with willful choler meeting

Makes my flesh tremble in their different greeting.

I will withdraw: but this instruction shall

(Fading) Now seeming sweet, convert to bitter gall.

MUSIC: *Swells a moment, then subsides under.*

NARRATOR: At the ball, Romeo continues to dance with Lord Capulet's beautiful young daughter, Juliet.

ROMEO *(Tenderly)*: If I profane with my unworthiest hand

This holy shrine, the gentle fine is this;

My lips, two blushing pilgrims, ready stand

To smooth that rough touch with a tender kiss.

JULIET *(Softly)*: Good pilgrim, you do wrong your hands too much,

Which mannerly devotion shows in this;

For saints have hands that pilgrims' hands do touch,

And palm to palm is holy palmers' kiss.

ROMEO: Have not saints lips? And holy palmers too?

JULIET: Aye, pilgrim. Lips that they must use in prayer.

NURSE (*Fading on*): Madam, your mother craves a word with you.

JULIET (*Fading*): I go at once, to hear my lady's words.

ROMEO: What is her mother?

NURSE: Marry, bachelor,
Her mother is the lady of the house.

ROMEO: The lady of the house! Is she a Capulet?
O dear account! My life is my foe's debt.

CAPULET (*Fading on*): Nay, gentlemen, prepare not to be gone;
We have a trifling foolish banquet towards.

ROMEO: Nay, good my host. We must!
(*Fading*) Mercutio, come!

CAPULET (*Fading*): More torches here! Good night! It waxes late!

JULIET (*In close*): Come hither, Nurse. What is yond gentleman?

NURSE: I know not, Madam Juliet.

JULIET: Go ask his name. If he be married,
My grave is like to be my wedding bed.

NURSE (*Fading on*): His name is Romeo, and a Montague,
The only son of your great enemy!

JULIET (*In despair*): My only love sprung from my only hate!
Too early seen unknown, and known too late!
Prodigious birth of love it is to me,
That I must love a loathed enemy.

NURSE (*Taken aback*): What's this, Juliet? What's this?

JULIET: A rhyme I learned even now, of one I danced withal.

CAPULET (*Far off mike*): Juliet!

NURSE: Anon, anon! Come, let's away. The strangers all
    are gone.

MUSIC: *Melancholy theme, in and under.*

NARRATOR: Too full of his new love and thoughts of beau-
    tiful Juliet, Romeo does not join Mercutio after the
    ball, but slips into the Capulet orchard, to breathe the
    perfumed air, sigh beneath the moon, and gaze up at
    the few lights left burning in the windows of the great
    mansion.

ROMEO: O, that my love be captured by my foe,
    And being held a foe, I have not access
    To breathe such vows as lovers use to swear;
    I must content myself with standing here,
    In darkness, 'neath my lady's balcony.
    But soft! What light through yonder window breaks?
    It is the east, and Juliet is the sun!
    It is my lady; O, it is my love!
    O, that she knew she were!
    See, how she leans her cheek upon her hand!
    O, that I were a glove upon that hand,
    That I might touch that cheek.

JULIET (*Off mike*): Ay me!

ROMEO: She speaks! O, speak again, bright angel!

JULIET (*Sighing*): O Romeo, Romeo! Wherefore art thou,
    Romeo?
    Deny thy father and refuse thy name;
    Or, if thou wilt not, be but sworn my love,
    And I'll no longer be a Capulet.
    'Tis but thy name that is my enemy;
    Thou art thyself though, not a Montague.
    What's in a name? That which we call a rose
    By any other name would smell as sweet.

Romeo, beloved, doff thy name,
And for thy name, which is no part of thee,
Take all myself.

ROMEO (*Boldly*): I take thee at thy word.
Call me but love, and I'll be new baptized;
Henceforth, I never will be Romeo.

JULIET: My ears have yet not drunk a hundred words
Of thy tongue's uttering, yet I know the sound:
Art thou not Romeo, and a Montague?

ROMEO: Neither, fair maid, if either thee dislike.

JULIET: This place is death, considering who thou art,
If any of my kinsmen find thee here.

ROMEO: And but thou love me, let them find me here!

JULIET: Although I joy in thee, sweet Montague,
I have no joy of this contract tonight:
It is too rash, too unadvised, too sudden.
This bud of love, by summer's ripening breath,
May prove a beauteous flower when next we meet.
Sweet, good night!

ROMEO: O, wilt thou leave me so unsatisfied?

JULIET: What satisfaction canst thou have tonight?

ROMEO: The exchange of thy love's faithful vow for mine.

JULIET: I gave thee mine before thou didst request it.
Three words, dear Romeo, and good night indeed.
If that thy bent of love be honorable,
Thy purpose marriage, send me word tomorrow,
By one that I'll procure to come to thee,
Where and what time thou wilt perform the rite,
And all my fortunes at thy foot I'll lay,
And follow thee, my lord, throughout the world.

NURSE (*Far off mike*): Ladybird! Madam!

JULIET (*Tenderly*): A thousand times good night!

ROMEO: A thousand times the worse, to want thy light.

JULIET: Good night, good night! Parting is such sweet sorrow

That I shall say good night till it be morrow.

MUSIC: *Romantic theme, in and under.*

NARRATOR: The following day, Juliet sends her Nurse to find young Romeo to discover if he had been serious in his protestations of love the night before.

NURSE: I pray thy pardon, sir, for interruption.

But canst tell me where to find young Romeo?

ROMEO: I am the youngest of that name, good woman.

NURSE: If you be he, sir, I desire to talk,

In confidence, about my lady, Juliet.

ROMEO: Good Nurse, commend me to thy lady mistress,

And bid the beauteous Juliet to devise

Some means to come to shrift this afternoon;

And there she shall at Friar Laurence' cell

Be shrived and married. Here is for thy pains.

NURSE: This afternoon, sir? Well, she shall be there.

ROMEO: Farewell; commend me to thy lady.

NURSE (*Fading*): I warrant thee, I shall, a thousand times.

MUSIC: *Ecclesiastical theme, in and under.*

NARRATOR: That afternoon, Romeo goes to Friar Laurence and informs him of his desire to be married to Juliet. The good priest, seeing in the marriage the possibility of reconciling the enmity of the Capulets and Montagues, is highly pleased, and agrees to marry them as soon as Juliet should appear.

FRIAR LAURENCE: So smile the heavens upon this holy act

That after-hours with sorrow chide us not!

ROMEO: Amen, amen! But come what sorrow can,

Do thou but close our hands with holy words,

Then love-devouring death do what he dare,

It is enough I may but call her mine.

FRIAR LAURENCE: Here comes the lady. O, so light a foot!

JULIET (*Fading on*): Good even to my ghostly confessor.

FRIAR LAURENCE: Romeo shall thank thee, daughter, for us both.

JULIET: As much to him, else is his thanks too much.

FRIAR LAURENCE: Come, come with me, and we will make short work;

For, by your leaves, you shall not stay alone

Till holy church incorporate two in one.

MUSIC: *Romantic theme, in and under.*

NARRATOR: And so, in secret, Juliet of Capulet becomes the bride of Romeo of Montague. Shortly thereafter, Tybalt, a cousin to Juliet, who had been offended by seeing Romeo at the Capulet ball, encounters Romeo's kinsman, Mercutio, in the central square of the city.

TYBALT (*Fading on, angrily*): Mercutio, good day. A word with you.

MERCUTIO: Only a word, Tybalt Capulet?

Could you couple it not with a blow?

TYBALT: Mercutio, I simply wish to know . . .

But, peace be with you, sir. Here comes my man.

MERCUTIO: 'Tis Romeo; he wears your livery not!

TYBALT: Romeo, the love I bear thee can afford

No better term than this—thou art a villain.

ROMEO (*Fading on, controlling himself*): Tybalt, the reason that I have to love thee

Doth much excuse the appertaining rage

To such a greeting; villain am I none.

TYBALT: Boy, this shall not excuse the injuries

That thou hast done me; therefore turn and draw.

ROMEO: I do protest, I never injured thee.

And so, good Capulet—which name I tender

As dearly as mine own—be satisfied.

MERCUTIO (*Angrily*): O calm, dishonorable, vile submis-
mission!

Tybalt, you rat-catcher, draw your arms!

TYBALT: I am for you!

SOUND: *Clash of foils.*

ROMEO: Gentlemen, for shame, forbear this outrage!

Tybalt, Mercutio, the prince expressly hath

Forbid this bandying in Verona's streets:

Hold, Tybalt! Good Mercutio!

MERCUTIO (*Gasps suddenly*): I am hurt!

A plague on both your houses! I am sped!

They have made worms' meat of me: I have it,

And soundly too: your houses . . . !

SOUND: *Body falling.*

ROMEO: My friend and kinsman, brave Mercutio, dead!

Now, Tybalt, take the "villain" back again

That late thou gavest me; for Mercutio's soul

Is but a little way above our heads,

Staying for thine to keep him company.

Either thou, or I, or both, must go with him.

TYBALT: This shall decide that!

SOUND: *Clash of foils.*

TYBALT (*Gasps*): There! I'm hurt! I fear that I am slain.

Slain by Romeo, the Montague.

SOUND: *Body falling.*

MUSIC: *Dramatic theme, in and under.*

NARRATOR: So Tybalt and Mercutio both are killed. The
Prince, in anger that the peace had been so broken,
banishes Romeo to far-off Mantua. The news spreads

fast; and soon, the new-made bride, fair Juliet, learns from her Nurse of her cousin's death, and husband's punishment.

NURSE (*Fading on, moaning*): Ah, well-a-day! He's dead, he's dead, he's dead!

We are undone, lady, we are undone.

JULIET: Can Heaven be so envious?

NURSE: Romeo can, though Heaven cannot.

Whoever would have thought it? Romeo!

JULIET: What devil art thou that dost torment me thus? Hath Romeo slain himself?

NURSE: O Tybalt! Tybalt! The best friend I had! That ever I should live to see thee dead!

JULIET: What storm is this that blows so contrary? Is Romeo slaughtered and is Tybalt dead? My dear-loved cousin and my dearer lord? O, who is living, if those two are gone?

NURSE: Tybalt is gone, and Romeo banished; Romeo that killed him, he is banished, Banished by the order of the Prince.

JULIET: O God! Did Romeo's hand shed Tybalt's blood?

NURSE: It did, it did; alas the day, it did!

JULIET: O, serpent heart, hid with a flowering face! Beautiful tyrant, fiend angelical!

NURSE: O, shame come to Romeo!

JULIET: Blistered be thy tongue!

NURSE: Will you speak well of him that kill'd your cousin?

JULIET: Shall I speak ill of him that is my husband?

NURSE: Hie to your chamber, then: I'll find Romeo, To comfort you: I wot well where he is. Hark ye, your Romeo will be here at night: I'll to him; he is hid at Laurence' cell.

JULIET: O, find him! Give this ring to my true knight,
And bid him come to take his last farewell.

MUSIC: *Tragic theme, in and under.*

NARRATOR: That night, the banished Romeo creeps in the
dark stillness to take his farewell of his bride.

JULIET (*Softly, tenderly*): Wilt thou be gone? It is not yet
near day.

It was the nightingale, and not the lark,

That pierced the fearful hollow of thine ear.

ROMEO: It was the lark, the herald of the morn.

I must be gone and live, or stay and die.

Come death, and welcome! Juliet wills it so.

How is't, my soul? Let's talk. It is not day.

JULIET: It is, it is! Hie hence, be gone, away.

O, now be gone, more light and light it grows.

ROMEO: More light and light: more dark and dark our
woes.

NURSE (*Calling from off mike in a whisper*): Madam!

JULIET: Nurse?

NURSE: Your lady mother is coming to your chamber.

JULIET: Then, window, let day in, and let life out.

Romeo, thou must leave for Mantua,

Under the order of our city's Prince.

ROMEO: Farewell, farewell. One kiss, and I'll descend.

JULIET: O, think'st thou we shall ever meet again?

ROMEO: I doubt it not; and all these woes shall serve

For sweet discourses in our time to come. Adieu!

MUSIC: *Unhappy theme, in and under.*

NARRATOR: With her cousin dead and husband banished,
Juliet is inconsolable. Not understanding the real reason
for her grief, her father, Lord Capulet, plans for her to
marry a rich nobleman, the County Paris.

CAPULET: How now, my daughter Juliet. Still in tears?
   Still grieving for thy cousin Tybalt's death?
   Come, come, my daughter. Dry your eyes awhile.
JULIET: Yet let me weep for such a feeling loss.
CAPULET: I bring thee happy news to dry thy eyes.
   Marry, my child, early next Thursday morn,
   The gallant, young and noble gentleman,
   The County Paris, at Saint Peter's Church,
   Shall happily make thee there a joyful bride.
JULIET: A bride! O, Father, pray that word unsay.
   No, no, I will have none, aye, none of him.
CAPULET (*Angrily*): How! You will none? Do you not give
      me thanks?
   Are you not proud? Do you not count you blest,
   Unworthy as you are, that we have wrought
   So worthy a gentleman to be your bridegroom?
JULIET: Proud can I never be of what I hate:
   But thankful even for hate that is meant love.
CAPULET: Thank me no thankings, nor proud me no
      prouds.
   But fettle your fine joints 'gainst Thursday next,
   To go with Paris to Saint Peter's Church,
   Or I will drag thee on a hurdle thither.
   An you be mine, I'll give you to my friend;
   An you be not, hang, beg, starve, die in the streets,
   For, by my soul, I'll ne'er acknowledge thee,
   Nor what is mine shall never do thee good.
   Trust to't, bethink you; I'll not be forsworn.
MUSIC: *Dramatic theme, in and under.*
NARRATOR: Not knowing which way to turn, Juliet goes,
   once more, to holy Friar Laurence's cell, to seek advice.
JULIET (*Fading on, miserably*): Good Friar Laurence, give
   my grief your ear.

To you, and you alone, I turn for help.

FRIAR LAURENCE: Ah, Juliet, I already know thy grief;
I hear thou must on Thursday next be married.

JULIET: Tell me not, Friar, that thou hear'st of this,
Unless thou tell me how I may prevent it.
If in thy wisdom thou canst give no help,
Then with this knife I'll help me presently.
God joined my heart and Romeo's, thou our hands;
Now, holy Friar Laurence, give me counsel.

FRIAR LAURENCE: Hold, daughter; I do spy a kind of hope,
Which craves as desperate an execution
As that is desperate which we would prevent.

JULIET: O, bid me leap, rather than marry Paris,
From off the battlements of yonder tower,
And I will do it without fear or doubt,
To live an unstain'd wife to my sweet love.

FRIAR LAURENCE: Hold then; go home, be merry, give consent
To marry Paris: Wednesday is tomorrow;
Tomorrow night, look that thou lie alone.
Take thou this vial, being then in bed,
And this distilled liquor drink thou off:
When presently through all thy veins shall run
A drowsy humor, simulating death.
And in this borrow'd likeness of shrunk death
Thou shalt continue two and forty hours,
And then awake, as from a pleasant sleep.
On thy marriage morn, they'll find thee dead.
Then, as the manner of our country is,
Thou shalt be borne, uncovered, to the tomb.
In the mean time, against thou shalt awake,
Shall Romeo by my letters know our drift:
And hither shall he come: and he and I

Will watch thy waking, and that very night
Shall Romeo bear thee hence to Mantua.

JULIET: Give me, give me the vial of liquid death.
Love give me strength, and strength shall help afford.
Farewell, dear Father!

MUSIC: *Dramatic theme, in and under.*

NARRATOR: Seeing it as her only escape, Juliet does as she is instructed. The next morning—that day which was to have been her wedding day—her Nurse comes early to rouse her from her bed.

NURSE (*Calling off mike*): Mistress! What, mistress! Juliet! Ladybird!
(*Fading on*) Why, lamb! Why, lady! Fie, you slug-a-bed!
Madam, Juliet, 'tis your marriage day.
I must needs wake you. Lady! Lady! Lady!
(*Shrieks*) What's this? Alas, alas! My lady's dead!

CAPULET (*Fading on*): What noise is here?

NURSE (*In tears*): O lamentable day!

CAPULET: For shame, bring Juliet forth; her lord is come.

NURSE: She's dead, deceased, she's dead; alack the day!

CAPULET: Her blood is settled . . . and her joints are stiff.
Death lies on her like an untimely frost
Upon the sweetest flower of all the field.

FRIAR LAURENCE (*Fading on*): Come, is the bride ready to go to church?

CAPULET (*Mournfully*): Ready to go, but never to return.
Death is my son-in-law, death is my heir;
My daughter he hath wedded. Juliet's dead!
Accurst, unhappy, wretched, hateful day!

FRIAR LAURENCE: Dry up your tears, and as the custom is,
Give word to bear the corpse unto the tomb.

Sir, go you in, and madam, go with him;
Make Lady Capulet, and Paris, 'ware,
To follow this fair corpse unto her grave:
The heavens do lour upon you for some ill;
Move them no more by crossing their high will.

MUSIC: *Stately theme, in and under.*

NARRATOR: Word of Juliet's death spreads rapidly; and within a short time, it is to reach even Romeo, who lonely in his banishment in Mantua, pines eagerly for news of his lovely bride.

ROMEO: How long, these exiled days in Mantua.
Each minute from my Juliet seems a year.
But here's news from Verona! Balthasar!
Welcome, my servant. How fares Juliet?

BALTHASAR (*Fading on*): Her body sleeps in Capel's monument,
And her immortal part with angels lives.
I saw her laid low in her kindred's vault,
And presently took post to tell it you:
O, pardon me for bringing these ill news,
Since you did leave it for my office, sir.

ROMEO: O, cursed Heavens! Is it even so?
My love, my Juliet dead? Hie, get thee gone!
Hire me horses; I'll be with thee straight!

MUSIC: *Turbulent theme, in and under.*

NARRATOR: Believing his servant's word of Juliet's death, the heartbroken Romeo makes his way back to Verona, and to the tomb of the Capulets.

SOUND: *A rusty lock, then iron doors squeaking on rusty hinges.*

ROMEO (*On echo mike, if possible*): How dank a tomb, how dark a vault is this.

O, cruel resting place for Juliet!
And there lies she. Ah, dear Juliet,
Why art thou yet so fair? Shall I believe
That unsubstantial death is amorous,
And keeps thee here to be his paramour?
For fear of that, I shall stay with thee.
Here will I remain. Eyes, look your last!
Arms, take your last embrace! And lips, O you
The doors of breath, seal with a righteous kiss
A dateless bargain to engrossing death.
Here's to my love! I drink this poison off!
(*Gasps*) The drugs are quick! Thus with a kiss, I die.
SOUND: *Body falling.*
FRIAR LAURENCE (*Fading on*): Saint Francis be my speed!
   I pray there's time!
   I must arrive in time to meet him. (*Gasps*) Romeo!
   What's this? Is Romeo here . . . and is he dead?
JULIET (*As arising from sleep*): O comfortable friar!
   Where is my lord?
   I do remember well where I should be,
   And there I am: where is my Romeo?
SOUND: *Voices far off mike.*
FRIAR LAURENCE: I hear some noise. Lady, come from
   here.
   A greater power than we can contradict
   Hath thwarted our intents: come, come away.
   Thy husband in thy bosom there lies dead.
   Stay not to question, for the watch is coming.
   (*Fading*) Come, go, good Juliet; I dare no longer stay.
JULIET: Go, get thee hence, for I will not away.
   What's here? A cup, closed in my true love's hand?
   Poison, I see, hath been his timeless end:

O churl! Drunk all, and left no friendly drop
To help me after? I will kiss thy lips;
Haply some poison yet doth hang on them,
To make me die with a restorative.
Thy lips are warm.

PRINCE (*Off mike*): Lead, boy; which way?

JULIET: Yea, noise? Then I'll be brief. O, happy dagger!
This is thy sheath! (*Gasps*) There rust, and let me die.

BALTHASAR (*Fading on*): This is the place; there, where
the torch doth burn.

PRINCE (*Fading on*): What misadventure is so early up,
That calls our person from our early rest?

CAPULET (*Fading on*): The people in the street cry Romeo,
And others shriek out Juliet, and all run
With open outcry to our monument.
What should it be that they so shriek abroad?
O lord! O heavens, see how my daughter bleeds!

PRINCE: Here comes old Montague, father to Romeo.
Come, Montague; for thou art early up,
To see thy son and heir more early down.

MONTAGUE: Alas, my liege, my wife is dead tonight;
Grief of my son's exile hath stopp'd her breath.
What further woe conspires against mine age?

PRINCE: Look, and thou shalt see.
Let someone tell the tale of what has passed!

FRIAR LAURENCE: I am best fit to tell the sorry tale.
Romeo, there dead, was husband to that Juliet.
And she, there dead, that Romeo's faithful wife.
I married them; and their stol'n marriage-day
Was Tybalt's dooms-day, whose untimely death
Banish'd the new-made bridegroom from this city;

For whom, and not for Tybalt, Juliet pined.
To avoid her marriage to the County Paris,
I gave to her, as tutored by my art,
A sleeping potion, which wrought on her
The form of death. Meantime I writ to Romeo,
To help to take her from her borrow'd grave.
By some unhappy accident, that letter
Never reached the husband, Romeo.
I came to fetch poor Juliet to my cell,
But when I came, some minute ere the time
Of her unwaking, here, beside her, lay
True Romeo, dead beyond a hope.
She wakes, and I entreated her to fly . . .
But then a noise did scare me from the tomb,
And, desperate lady, she then killed herself.

CAPULET: O, brother Montague, give me thy hand:
This is my daughter's jointure, for no more
Can I demand.

MONTAGUE: But I can give thee more,
For I will raise her statue in pure gold,
Poor sacrifice of our past enmity.

PRINCE: A glooming peace this morning with it brings;
The sun for sorrow will not show its head:
Go hence, to have more talk of these sad things;
Some shall be pardoned, and some punished.
For never was a story of more woe,
Than this of Juliet, and her Romeo.

MUSIC: *Tragic theme, full to finish.*

THE END

Julius Caesar

Characters

SOOTHSAYER
JULIUS CAESAR
CASSIUS
BRUTUS
LUCIUS
CALPURNIA

MARK ANTONY
MEN, *three*
WOMEN, *two*
PINDARUS
SOLDIER
STRATO

SOOTHSAYER (*In ominous tones*): Caesar! Caesar! Beware the Ides of March!

MUSIC: *Forbidding theme, in and under.*

NARRATOR: Against the cold and classic columns of the Roman Senate, William Shakespeare set the tragedy of one of the greatest generals of all time, Julius Caesar, and of the men who surrounded him. Returning to Rome in triumph over Pompey, Caesar is greeted by the enthusiastic populace, who cheer and honor him. In the midst of his triumphal march into the city, however, a voice, high and shrill, calls out his name in such a pressing tone that the great general stops the procession to listen.

SOUND: *Clamor of mob in background.*

SOOTHSAYER (*Off mike*): Caesar!

CAESAR: Ha! Who calls?

CASSIUS (*Calling out*): Bid every noise be still. Peace ho! Caesar speaks!

SOUND: *Clamor of mob subsides.*

CAESAR: Who is it in the press that calls on me?
I hear a tongue, shriller than all the music,
Cry "Caesar." Speak: Caesar is turned to hear.

SOOTHSAYER (*Off mike, warningly*): Beware the Ides of March!

CAESAR: What man is that?

CASSIUS: A soothsayer bids you beware the Ides of March!

CAESAR: He is a dreamer; let us leave him; pass.

MUSIC: *Ominous theme, in and under.*

NARRATOR: And so, not heeding the warning to beware the Ides of March, Julius Caesar marches on to the cheers of the common people. While the mob rejoices in Caesar, however, a faction of nobles, headed by Cassius, fear Caesar's ambition and his sudden rise in public favor. They form a conspiracy against Caesar's life; and Cassius, the ringleader, approaches Brutus trying to win him to their cause. Brutus is so widely known as a man of pure ideals and motives that Cassius counts on Brutus' reputation absolving all the conspirators of blame.

SOUND: *Burst of shouting and applause of mob in background.*

BRUTUS: What means this shouting, Cassius? I do fear the people choose Caesar for their king.

CASSIUS: Aye, Brutus, do you fear it? Then must I think you would not have it so.

BRUTUS: I would not, Cassius, yet I love him well.
  But wherefore do you hold me here so long?
  What is it that you would impart to me?
SOUND: *Another shout from the mob.*
BRUTUS: Another general shout!
  I do believe that these applauses are
  For some new honors that are heaped on Caesar.
CASSIUS: Why, man, he doth bestride the narrow world
  Like a Colossus, and we petty men
  Walk under his huge legs and peep about
  To find ourselves dishonourable graves.
  Men at some time are masters of their fates:
  The fault, dear Brutus, is not in our stars
  But in ourselves, that we are underlings.
BRUTUS: What mean you, Cassius, friend; I bid you speak!
CASSIUS: Brutus and Caesar: what should be in that Caesar?
  Why should that name be sounded more than yours?
  Write them together, yours is as fair a name;
  Sound them, it doth become the mouth as well.
  Now in the names of all the gods at once,
  Upon what meat doth this our Caesar feed,
  That he is grown so great? Age, thou art shamed!
  Rome, thou hast lost the breed of noble bloods!
  When could they say till now that talked of Rome
  That her wide walls encompassed but one man?
BRUTUS: What you would work me to, I have some aim:
  How I have thought of this and of these times,
  I shall recount hereafter; for this present,
  I would not, so with love I might entreat you,
  Be any further moved. What you have said
  I will consider; what you have to say

I will with patience hear, and find a time
Both meet to hear and answer such high things.
(*Fading*) For this time, worthy Cassius, I will leave you.

CASSIUS (*In close*): Well, Brutus, thou art noble; yet, I see
Thy honorable metal may be wrought
From that it is disposed: therefore it is meet
That noble minds keep ever with their likes;
For who so firm that cannot be seduced?
Caesar doth bear me hard; but he loved Brutus:
If I were Brutus now and he were Cassius,
He should not humor me. I will this night,
In several hands, in at his windows throw,
As if they came from several citizens,
Writings, all tending to the great opinion
That Rome holds of his name, wherein obscurely
Caesar's ambition shall be glanced at:
And after this, let Caesar seat him sure;
For we will shake him, or worse days endure.

MUSIC: *Dramatic theme, in and under.*

NARRATOR: Having planted the seeds of discontent with
Caesar in the noble Brutus' mind, Cassius forges several
anonymous letters and throws them in at Brutus' window at night, to reinforce that nobleman's suspicions,
fears and doubts.

BRUTUS (*Calling out*): Lucius! Is the taper in my study
lighted?

LUCIUS (*Fading on*): The taper burneth in your closet,
sir.
Searching the window for a flint I found
This letter thus sealed up, and I am sure
It did not lie there when I went to bed.

BRUTUS: Give me it here. Is not tomorrow, boy, the Ides of March?

LUCIUS: I know not, sir.

BRUTUS: Look in the calendar, and bring me word.

LUCIUS (*Fading*): I will, sir.

SOUND: *Paper being torn open.*

BRUTUS (*Reading*): "Brutus, thou sleep'st: awake and see thyself.

Shall Rome,— (*Reading to himself*) Speak, strike, redress.

Brutus, thou sleep'st: awake."

Such instigations have been often dropped

Where I have took them up.

"Shall Rome, etc.," Thus must I piece it out:

Shall Rome stand under one man's awe? What, Rome?

My ancestors did from the streets of Rome

The Tarquin drive, when he was called a king.

"Speak, strike, redress." Am I entreated

To speak and strike? O Rome, I make thee promise,

If the redress will follow, thou receivest

Thy full petition at the hand of Brutus!

LUCIUS (*Fading on*): Sir, March is wasted fifteen days.

BRUTUS: 'Tis good. Get you to bed; it is not day.

LUCIUS (*Fading*): I will, my lord. Good night.

BRUTUS: Since Cassius first did whet me against Caesar

I have not slept.

Between the acting of a dreadful thing

And the first motion, all the interim is

Like a phantasma or a hideous dream:

The genius and the mortal instruments

Are then in council, and the state of man,

Like to a little kingdom, suffers then
The nature of an insurrection.

Music: *Portentous theme, in and under.*

Narrator: The anonymous letters having convinced
Brutus of Caesar's potential danger to Rome, he resolves
to join the conspiracy, and the next day is welcomed
to the band of assassins by the sly Cassius.

Cassius: Good Brutus, hail; your joining in our plan
Has met with pleasure of the highest sort.
Before we proceed, I would a question ask:
Shall no man else be touched, but only Caesar?
I think it is not meet Mark Antony
Should outlive Caesar. Let them fall together,
For in life they stand firm friends together.

Brutus: Our course will seem too bloody, Caius Cassius,
To cut the head off and then hack the limbs,
Like wrath in death and envy afterwards;
For Antony is but a limb of Caesar.
Let us be sacrificers, but not butchers, Cassius.
As for Mark Antony, think not of him;
For he can do no more than Caesar's arm
When Caesar's head is off.

Cassius: Yet I fear him,
For in the ingrafted love he bears to Caesar—

Brutus: Alas, good Cassius, do not think of him:
If he love Caesar, all that he can do
Is to himself, take thought and die for Caesar.
There is no fear in him; let him not die;
For he will live and laugh at this hereafter.

Music: *Ominous theme, in and under.*

Narrator: So Brutus convinces Cassius that it will be
harmless to allow Mark Antony to live when Caesar is

dead. The next day is the Ides of March. As Caesar prepares to leave home for the Senate, his wife, Calpurnia, mindful of the soothsayer's prophecy, attempts to persuade him to remain at home and avert catastrophe.

SOUND: *Thunder and rain softly in background.*

CALPURNIA: What mean you, Caesar? Think you to walk forth?

You shall not stir out of your house today.

CAESAR: Caesar shall forth. The Ides of March are come.

CALPURNIA: Aye, husband Caesar, come but not yet gone.

Last night was filled with strange and awful deeds.

The noise of battle hurtled in the air,

Horses did neigh, and dying men did groan,

And ghosts did shriek and squeal about the streets.

O Caesar! These things are beyond all use,

And I do fear them.

CAESAR: Yet, wife Calpurnia, Caesar shall go forth,

For these predictions, awful though they be,

Are to the world in general as to Caesar.

CALPURNIA: When beggars die, there are no comets seen;

The heavens themselves blaze forth the death of princes.

CAESAR: Cowards die many times before their deaths;

The valiant never taste of death but once.

Give me my robe, Calpurnia; I will go.

MUSIC: *Portentous theme, in and under.*

NARRATOR: As the soothsayer predicted, the Ides of March brings tragedy to Julius Caesar. As he approaches the senate-house, he is confronted by the band of conspirators, who watch him silently, grimly.

CAESAR *(Surprised)*: Gentlemen, what brings thee before me? Why do you stop me, here in the senate-house?

Speak, Casca, Cinna, Trebonius; Cassius, speak! What? Swords drawn?

SOUND: *Swords being unsheathed.*

CASSIUS (*With force*): Speak, hands, for me! Dagger find your mark! Death to the tyrant!

AD LIB: *Tumult of conspirators.*

CAESAR (*Gasping in pain*): Ligarius . . . and Metellus Cimber? Do you stab me also? (*In despair*) *Et tu, Brute?* Then fall, Caesar!

CASSIUS (*Loudly*): Caesar, tyrant Caesar, is now dead!

MUSIC: *Tragic theme, in and under.*

NARRATOR: Thus Julius Caesar is assassinated at the hands of the conspirators. In jubilation, Cassius shouts the news through the streets.

CASSIUS (*Shouting jubilantly*): Liberty! Freedom! Tyranny is dead!

Run hence, proclaim, cry it about the streets!

People and senators, be not affrighted;

Fly not; stand still: ambition's debt is paid.

BRUTUS: But here comes Caesar's friend, Mark Antony.

ANTONY (*Fading on*): O mighty Caesar! dost thou lie so low?

Are all thy conquests, glories, triumphs, spoils,

Shrunk to this little measure? Fare thee well.

BRUTUS: Antony, we know that you must grieve,

For Caesar was your love. But this we ask:

Only be patient till we have appeased

The multitude, beside themselves with fear,

And then we will deliver to you the cause

Why I, that did love Caesar, when I struck him,

Have thus proceeded.

ANTONY: I doubt not of your wisdom.
  Let each man render me his bloody hand.
CASSIUS: Say, what compact mean you to have with us?
  Will you be pricked in number of our friends,
  Or shall we on, and not depend on you?
ANTONY: Friends am I with you all and love you all,
  Upon this hope that you shall give me reasons
  Why and wherein Caesar was dangerous.
BRUTUS: Or else were this a savage spectacle:
  Our reasons are so full of good regard
  That were you, Antony, the son of Caesar,
  You should be satisfied.
ANTONY: That's all I seek:
  And am moreover suitor that I may
  Produce his body to the market-place,
  And in the pulpit, as becomes a friend,
  Speak in the order of his funeral.
BRUTUS: You shall, Mark Antony.
MUSIC: *Dramatic theme, in and under.*
NARRATOR: Caesar's body is carried to the market-place,
  where Brutus explains to the populace his reasons for
  the assassination. Mark Antony, friend to the dead
  Caesar, accompanies his body, having been promised
  by Brutus the right to preach a funeral oration over the
  corpse.
SOUND: *Murmur of mob in background.*
BRUTUS: Romans, countrymen, and lovers! hear me for
  my cause, and be silent, that you may hear. If there be
  any in this assembly, any dear friend of Caesar's, to him
  I say that Brutus' love to Caesar was no less than his.
  If then that friend demand why Brutus rose against

Caesar, this is my answer— Not that I loved Caesar less, but that I loved Rome more. Had you rather Caesar were living, and die all slaves, than that Caesar were dead, to live all free men? As Caesar loved me, I weep for him; as he was fortunate, I rejoice at it; as he was valiant, I honor him; but as he was ambitious, I slew him. There is tears for his love; joy for his fortune; honor for his valor; and death for his ambition. Who is here so base that would be a bondman? Who is here so rude that would not be a Roman? Who is here so vile that will not love his country? If any, speak: for him have I offended. I pause for a reply.

MOB (*Ad lib, loudly calling out*): None, Brutus, none!

BRUTUS: Then none have I offended. I have done no more to Caesar than you shall do to Brutus. Here comes his body, mourned by Mark Antony. With this I depart— that as I slew my best lover for the good of Rome, I have the same dagger for myself, when it shall please my country to need my death.

MOB (*Ad lib*): Live, Brutus! Live! Live!

1ST MAN: Let him be Caesar!

2ND WOMAN: Caesar's better parts shall be crowned in Brutus!

1ST WOMAN: We'll bring him to his house with shouts and clamors!

BRUTUS: My countrymen . . .

1ST MAN: Peace ho! Brutus speaks!

BRUTUS: Good countrymen, let me depart alone,
And for my sake, stay here with Antony:
Do grace to Caesar's corpse, and grace his speech,
Tending to Caesar's glories, which Mark Antony
By our permission is allowed to make.

2ND WOMAN: Stay! And let us hear Mark Antony!

MOB (*Ad lib*): Stay! Mark Antony! Listen!

ANTONY: Friends, Romans, countrymen, lend me your
    ears:

  I come to bury Caesar, not to praise him.

  The evil that men do lives after them;

  The good is oft interred with their bones;

  So let it be with Caesar. The noble Brutus

  Hath told you Caesar was ambitious:

  If it were so, it was a grievous fault,

  And grievously hath Caesar answered it.

  Here, under leave of Brutus and the rest,—

  For Brutus is an honorable man;

  So are they all, all honorable men,—

  Come I to speak in Caesar's funeral.

  He was my friend, faithful and just to me:

  But Brutus says he was ambitious;

  And Brutus is an honorable man.

  He hath brought many captives home to Rome,

  Whose ransoms did the general coffers fill:

  Did this in Caesar seem ambitious?

  When the poor have cried, Caesar hath wept:

  Ambition should be made of sterner stuff:

  Yet Brutus says he was ambitious;

  And Brutus is an honorable man.

  You all did see that on the Lupercal

  I thrice presented him a kingly crown,

  Which he did thrice refuse: was this ambition?

  Yet Brutus says he was ambitious;

  And, sure, he is an honorable man.

  I speak not to disprove what Brutus spoke,

  But here am I to speak what I do know.

You all did love him once, not without cause:
What cause withholds you then to mourn for him?
O judgment! thou art fled to brutish beasts,
And men have lost their reason. Bear with me;
My heart is in the coffin there with Caesar,
And I must pause till it come back to me.

2ND MAN: Methinks there is much reason in his sayings.

1ST WOMAN: Caesar has had great wrong!

3RD MAN: He would not take the crown. Is that ambition?

1ST MAN: There's not a nobler man in Rome than Antony.

2ND WOMAN: Poor soul! His eyes are red as fire with
weeping.

1ST MAN: Now mark him, he begins again to speak.

ANTONY: But yesterday the word of Caesar might
Have stood against the world: now lies he there,
And none so poor to do him reverence.
Now make a ring about the corpse of Caesar
And let me show you him they called tyrant.
Shall I descend? And will you give me leave?

MOB (Ad lib): Come down. Descend. You shall have leave.

ANTONY: Nay, press not so upon me; stand far off.

MOB (Ad lib): Stand back; room; bear back.

ANTONY: If you have tears, prepare to shed them now.
You all do know this mantle—
Look, in this place ran Cassius' dagger through:
See what a rent the envious Casca made:
Through this the well-beloved Brutus stabb'd;
And, as he pluckt his cursed steel away,
Mark how the blood of Caesar follow'd it;
For Brutus, as you know, was Caesar's angel:
Judge, O you gods, how dearly Caesar loved him!

This was the most unkindest cut of all;
For when the noble Caesar saw him stab,
Ingratitude, more strong than traitors' arms,
Quite vanquisht him; then burst his mighty heart;
And, in his mantle muffling up his face,
Even at the base of Pompey's statue,
Which all the while ran blood, great Caesar fell.
O, what a fall was there, my countrymen!
Then I, and you, and all of us fell down,
Whilst bloody treason flourisht over us.
O, now you weep; and, I perceive, you feel
The dint of pity: these are gracious drops.
Kind souls, what, weep you when you but behold
Our Caesar's vesture wounded? Look you here,
Here is himself, marr'd, as you see, with traitors.

1st WOMAN: O piteous spectacle!

2nd MAN: Most noble Caesar!

3rd MAN: We'll revenge his death!

1st MAN: We'll mutiny! We'll burn the house of Brutus!

Mob *(Ad lib)*: Revenge! To Brutus' house! Let not a traitor live!

Most noble Caesar! (*The angry voices of the mob fade away.*)

ANTONY (*In close*): Now let it work. Mischief, thou art afoot.

Take thou what course thou wilt.

MUSIC: *Dramatic, angry theme, in and under.*

NARRATOR: Stirred by Mark Antony's oratory, the people of Rome turn on Cassius, Brutus, and the conspirators, all of whom are forced to flee Rome. Antony, joining forces with another young noble, Octavius, sets out in pursuit of Cassius and Brutus, who are in camp near Sardis.

SOUND: *Drum roll, slightly off mike.*

BRUTUS: Come in, good Cassius. Welcome!
Now sit we close about this taper here,
And call in question our necessities.
Cassius, I have here received letters,
That young Octavius and Mark Antony
Come down upon us with a mighty power,
Bending their expedition toward Philippi.

CASSIUS: Myself have letters of the self-same tenor,
Concerning the newly-formed triumvirate,
Octavius, Antony and Lepidus.

BRUTUS: What do you think of marching to Philippi presently?

CASSIUS: I do not think it good.

BRUTUS: Your reason?

CASSIUS: This it is:
'Tis better that the enemy seek us:
So shall he waste his means, weary his soldiers,
Doing himself offense; whilst we lying still
Are full of rest, defense and nimbleness.

BRUTUS: Good reasons must of force give way to better.
The people 'twixt Philippi and this ground
Do stand but in forced affection.
The enemy, marching along by them,
By them shall make a fuller number up;
From which advantage we shall cut him off
If at Philippi we do face him there.
The deep of night has crept upon our talk,
And nature must obey necessity;
There is no more to say?

CASSIUS: No more. Good night. (*Fading*) Early tomorrow we will rise and hence.

BRUTUS: Noble, noble Cassius, good night and good repose. (*Calling*) Lucius, my gown! Here is my book. Let me see, is not the leaf turned down where I left reading? Here it is, I think.

MUSIC: *Eerie theme, sneak in and hold under.*

NARRATOR: As Brutus sits alone in his tent, tired and distressed, the room seems to grow suddenly darker, and a dim specter appears in the guise of the dead Julius Caesar.

BRUTUS: How ill this taper burns! Ha! who comes here?
I think it is the weakness of mine eyes
That shapes a monstrous apparition.
It comes upon me. Art thou any thing?
Art thou some god, some angel, or some devil,
That makest my blood cold, and my hair to stare?
Speak to me what thou art!

CAESAR (*In a ghostly, sepulchral tone*): Thy evil spirit, Brutus.

BRUTUS: Why comest thou?

CAESAR: To tell thee thou shalt see me at Philippi.

BRUTUS: Well; then I shall see thee again?

CAESAR (*Fading; mysteriously*): Aye, at Philippi.

BRUTUS: Why, I will see thee at Philippi then.
Now I have taken heart, thou vanishest.
Ill spirit, I would hold more talk with thee!

CAESAR (*Off mike*): At Philippi, Marcus Brutus. At Philipiiiii!

MUSIC: *Dramatic theme, in and under.*

NARRATOR: Mark Antony's troops meet with those of the conspirators at Philippi, and from the very outset it is

Antony who is victorious. In retreat, Cassius learns that Mark Antony has taken his tents, and standing on a hill with his servant, Pindarus, looking back at the flames, Cassius resolves to take his own life.

SOUND: *Battle noise softly in background throughout remainder of play.*

CASSIUS: O look, Pindarus, look!

PINDARUS: Fly further off, my lord, fly further off;
Mark Antony is in your tents, my lord:
Fly, therefore, noble Cassius, fly far off.

CASSIUS: This hill is far enough. Look, look, Pindarus;
Are those my tents where I perceive the fire?

PINDARUS: They are, my lord.

CASSIUS (*Despondently*): Come down; behold no more.
O, coward that I am, to live so long,
To see my own tents taken before my face!
Come hither, Sirrah!
In Parthia did I take thee prisoner;
And then I swore thee, saving of thy life,
That whatsoever I did bid thee do,
Thou shouldst attempt it. Come now, keep thy oath;
Now be a freeman; and with this good sword,
That ran through Caesar's bowels, search this bosom.
Stand not to answer: here, take thou the hilts;
And when my face is covered—as 'tis now,
Guide thou the sword. (*Gasps*) Caesar, thou art revenged,
Even with the sword that killed thee.

MUSIC: *Tragic theme, in and under.*

NARRATOR: Mark Antony's victory is complete. The few remaining troops of the conspirators are scattered in defeat. Preferring death to capture and dishonor, Brutus makes one last command upon his servant, Strato.

SOLDIER (*Off mike*): Fly, my lord, fly!

BRUTUS: Hence! I will follow!

I prithee, Strato, stay thou by thy lord:

Thou art a fellow of good respect;

Hold then my sword, and turn away thy face,

While I do run upon it. Wilt thou, Strato?

STRATO: Give me your hand first: fare you well, my lord.

BRUTUS: Farewell, good Strato. Caesar, now be still;

(*Gasps, dying*)

I killed not thee with half so good a will.

MUSIC: *Tragic theme, in and under.*

NARRATOR: Barely has Brutus breathed his final breath, when the conquering Mark Antony comes upon his body. He recognizes Strato as Brutus' servant at once, and questions him.

ANTONY (*Fading on*): What man is that? Strato, where is thy master?

STRATO: Free from the bondage most of us are in;

You conquerors can but make a fire of him;

For Brutus only overcame himself,

And no man else hath honor by his death.

ANTONY: How died your master, Strato?

STRATO: I held the sword, and he did run on it.

ANTONY: This was the noblest Roman of them all:

All the conspirators, save only he,

Did that they did in envy of great Caesar;

He only, in a general honest thought,

And common good to all, made one of them.

His life was gentle, and the elements

So mixed in him that Nature might stand up
And say to all the world, "This was a man!"
MUSIC: *Tragic theme, full to climactic finish.*

THE END

Hamlet

Characters

HORATIO	OPHELIA
BERNARDO	POLONIUS
KING CLAUDIUS	GHOST OF HAMLET'S FATHER
PRINCE HAMLET	A PLAYER
QUEEN GERTRUDE	A SERVANT
LAERTES	NARRATOR

NARRATOR: Against the bleak, forbidding stone walls of Elsinore, the royal castle in Denmark, William Shakespeare unfolded his stark and immortal drama, *Hamlet*.

MUSIC: *Short, stately fanfare.*

NARRATOR: Learning of his father's sudden death, Hamlet, young prince of Denmark, returns to the castle from Wittenberg, where he has been at school. The late king's brother, Claudius, has ascended the throne, and married the Queen, Hamlet's mother. This marriage robs Hamlet of his confidence in his mother, and leaves him completely alone in his grief. A rumor that the ghost of the late king has been seen before the castle gates only deepens the young prince's melancholy and isolation. As the play begins, it is midnight, and Bernardo, a sentinel, is keeping watch before the royal castle. Suddenly, Horatio, the closest friend of young Prince Hamlet, appears.

HORATIO (*Fading on*): Who's there?

BERNARDO: Nay, answer me. Stand and unfold yourself.
 What, is Horatio there?

HORATIO: A piece of him.

BERNARDO: Welcome, Horatio.

HORATIO: What! Has this thing appear'd again tonight?

BERNARDO: I have seen nothing, yet I still believe it.

HORATIO: Nay, Bernardo, 'tis your fantasy.
 I will not let belief take hold of me,
 Touching this dreaded sight.

BERNARDO: Peace! Break thee off!
 Look where it comes again!

HORATIO: In the same figure, like the king that's dead!

BERNARDO: Speak to't, Horatio. It would be spoke to.

HORATIO: What art thou that usurp'st this time of night,
 Together with that fair and warlike form
 In which the majesty of buried Denmark
 Did sometimes march? By heaven, I charge thee, speak.

BERNARDO: It is offended; see, it stalks away.

SOUND: *Cock crowing far off mike.*

BERNARDO (*Without pause*): How now, Horatio! You
 tremble, and look pale.
 Is it not like the king?

HORATIO: As thou art to thyself!

BERNARDO: It was about to speak when the cock crew.
 And then it started, like a guilty thing,
 And faded on the crowing of the cock.

HORATIO: But look! The morn in russet mantle clad
 Walks o'er the dew of yon high eastern hill.

Break we our watch up. Let us impart

What we have seen tonight unto young Hamlet.

This spirit, dumb to us, will speak to him.

MUSIC: *Solemn theme, in and under.*

NARRATOR: Thus, Horatio, convinced that he has seen the
ghost of the dead king, resolves to tell young Hamlet of
it. The following morning, Hamlet attends the King,
his Uncle Claudius, and the Queen, his mother, in a
room of state in the castle, along with many other
courtiers and lords of state.

MUSIC: *A flourish of trumpets.*

KING: Though yet of Hamlet our dear brother's death

The memory be green in all our hearts,

Yet so far hath discretion fought with nature

That we with wisest sorrow think on him,

Together with remembrance of ourselves.

Therefore our sometime sister, now our queen,

Have we, as 'twere with a defeated joy,

Taken to wife. Nor have we herein barr'd

Your better wisdoms, which have freely gone,

With this affair along. For all, our thanks.

But now, my cousin Hamlet, and my son . . .

HAMLET (*As an aside*): A little more than kin, and less
than kind.

KING: How is it that the clouds still hang on you?

HAMLET: Not so, my lord; I am too much i' the sun.

QUEEN: Good Hamlet, cast thy nighted color off,

And let thine eye look like a friend on Denmark.

Do not forever with thy vailed lids

Seek for thy noble father in the dust.

Thou know'st 'tis common; all that lives must die.

HAMLET: Ay, mother, it is—"common."

QUEEN: If it be,
  Why seems it so particular with thee?
HAMLET: "Seems," madam! Nay, it is! I know not "seems."
  'Tis not alone my solemn cloak, good mother,
  No, nor the fruitful river in the eye,
  Together with all forms, modes, shows of grief,
  That can denote me truly; these indeed "seem,"
  For they are actions that a man might play;
  But I have that within which passeth show;
  These but the trappings and the suits of woe.
KING: 'Tis sweet to mourn your buried father, Hamlet.
  But to persever in obstinate condolement,
  'Tis unmanly grief. We pray you, think of us
  As of a father. And for your intent
  In going back to school in Wittenberg,
  It is most retrograde to our desire.
QUEEN: Let not thy mother lose her prayers, Hamlet:
  I pray thee, stay with us. Go not to Wittenberg.
HAMLET: I shall in all my best obey you, madam.
KING: Why, 'tis a loving and a fair reply.
  This gentle and unforc'd accord of Hamlet
  Sits smiling to my heart. Come, all, away.
MUSIC: *Flourish of trumpets.*
NARRATOR: Alone, Hamlet gives way to private, brooding
  thoughts.
HAMLET: O, that this too too solid flesh would melt,
  Thaw, and resolve itself into a dew!
  Or that the Everlasting had not fix'd
  His canon 'gainst self-slaughter! O God! O God!
  How weary, stale, flat, and unprofitable
  Seems to me all the uses of this world.
  But two months dead! Nay, not so much, not two!

So excellent a king; that was, to this,
Hyperion to a satyr! So loving to my mother!
Heaven and earth! Why must I remember?
Why, she, his lady queen, would hang on him
As if increase of appetite had grown
By what it fed on; and yet, within a month—
Let me not think on't. Frailty, thy name is "woman."
O God! A beast that wants discourse of reason
Would have mourn'd longer. Married with mine uncle,
My father's brother! But no more like my father
Than I to Hercules. Within a month!
Ere yet the salt of most unrighteous tears
Had left the flushing in her eyes, she married.
It is not nor it cannot come to good!
But break, my heart, for I must hold my tongue.

NARRATOR: As Hamlet sits lost in thought, his faithful friend, Horatio, comes to him, to tell him of the appearance of the late king's ghost.

HORATIO (*Fading on*): Hail to your lordship!

HAMLET: I am glad to see you well.
Horatio! Or I do forget myself.
And what make you from Wittenberg, Horatio?

HORATIO: My lord, I came to see your father's funeral.

HAMLET: I think it was to see my mother's wedding.

HORATIO: Indeed, my lord, it follow'd hard upon.

HAMLET: Thrift, thrift, Horatio! The funeral baked meats
Did coldly furnish forth the marriage tables.
Would I had my dearest foe in Heaven
Ere I had seen that day, Horatio!
My father, methinks I see my father . . .

HORATIO: O, where, my lord?

HAMLET: In my mind's eye, Horatio.

HORATIO: Hamlet, I think I saw him yesternight.

HAMLET: Saw? Who?

HORATIO: My lord, the king your father.

HAMLET: The king my father! For God's love, let me hear.

HORATIO: Two nights together had the men at watch
　　Been thus encounter'd: a figure, like your father,
　　Appears before them, and with solemn march,
　　Goes slow and stately by them. This to me
　　In dreadful secrecy impart they did;
　　And I with them the third night kept the watch;
　　Where, as they had deliver'd, even so,
　　The apparition comes. I knew your father;
　　These hands are not more like.

HAMLET: But where was this?

HORATIO: My lord, upon the platform where we watched.

HAMLET: Did you not speak to it?

HORATIO: My lord, I did. But answer made it none.

HAMLET: 'Tis very strange.

HORATIO: As I do live, my honor'd lord, 'tis true.

HAMLET: I would I had been there, Horatio.
　　I'll watch tonight. Perchance 'twill walk again.

HORATIO: I warrant it will come again, good Hamlet.

HAMLET: If it assume my noble father's person,
　　I'll speak to it though hell itself should gape
　　And bid me hold my peace. So fare you well.
　　Upon the platform, 'twixt eleven and twelve,
　　I'll visit you.

HORATIO (*Fading*): My duty to your honor.

HAMLET: Your love, as mine to you. Farewell.
　　My father's spirit abroad! All is not well.
　　I doubt some foul play. Would the night were come!

Till then, sit still, my soul. Foul deeds will rise,
Though all the earth o'erwhelm them, to men's eyes.

MUSIC: *Mysterious theme, in and under.*

NARRATOR: Elsewhere in the castle, Laertes, a schoolmate
of Hamlet's, prepares to return to Wittenberg. He is
the son of Polonius, old Lord High Chamberlain, and
brother to Ophelia, a beautiful young girl to whom
Hamlet has paid court. Having prepared himself for his
journey, Laertes takes his leave of his sister.

LAERTES: Farewell, Ophelia. Let me hear from you.
For Hamlet, and the trifling of his favor,
Hold it a fashion and a toy in blood.
Perhaps he loves you now, but you must fear.
His greatness weighed, his will is not his own.
He may not, as unvalued persons do,
Carve for himself.

OPHELIA: I shall the effect of this good lesson keep
As watchman to my heart.

LAERTES: I stay too long. But here my father comes.

POLONIUS (*Fading on*): Yet here, Laertes! Abroad, abroad,
for shame!
The ship awaits. There—my blessing with thee.
And these few precepts in thy memory,
See thou character. Give thy thoughts no tongue,
Nor any unproportion'd thought his act.
Be thou familiar, but by no means vulgar.
Give every man thine ear, but few thy voice;
Take each man's censure, but reserve thy judgement.
Neither a borrower nor a lender be;
For loan oft loses both itself and friend,
And borrowing dulls the edge of husbandry.

This above all: to thine own self be true;
And it must follow, as the night the day,
Thou canst not then be false to any man.
Farewell! My blessing season this in thee!

LAERTES: Most humbly do I take my leave, my lord.
(*Fading*) Farewell, Ophelia; and remember well
What I have said.

OPHELIA (*Calling after him*): 'Tis in my memory locked,
And you yourself shall keep the key of it.

POLONIUS: What is it, Ophelia, he has said to you?

OPHELIA: So please you, something touching the Lord
Hamlet.

POLONIUS: Marry, well bethought!
'Tis told me he hath very oft of late
Given private time to you.
What is between you? Give me up the truth.

OPHELIA: He hath, my lord, of late made many tenders
Of his affection to me.

POLONIUS: Affection! Pooh! You speak like a green girl.
Do you believe his "tenders," as you call them?

OPHELIA: I do not know, good father, what to think.

POLONIUS: I would not, in plain terms, from this time
forth
Have you so slander any moment's leisure
As to give words or talk with the Lord Hamlet.
Look to't, I charge you. Come your ways.

OPHELIA: I shall obey, my lord.

MUSIC: *In and under.*

NARRATOR: That night, Hamlet accompanies his friend,
Horatio, to the place where the apparition had been
seen. Once again, the ghost of the dead king appears,
but refuses to speak, seeming to fear the presence of

Horatio. The ghost beckons Hamlet away; and the young prince resolves to follow to another part of the platform.

SOUND: *Wind whistling softly in background.*

HAMLET: Whither wilt thou lead me? Speak, I pray.

GHOST (*In sepulchral tones*): Mark me!

HAMLET: I will. Speak; I am bound to hear.

GHOST: So art thou to revenge, when thou shalt hear!

HAMLET: What?

GHOST: I am thy father's spirit,
  Doom'd for a certain time to walk the night.
  List, Hamlet! If thou didst thy father love—

HAMLET: O God!

GHOST: Revenge his foul and most unnatural murder.

HAMLET: Murder! Haste me to know't!

GHOST: Now, Hamlet, hear:
  'Tis given out that sleeping in my orchard,
  A serpent stung me. But know, thou noble youth,
  The serpent that did sting thy father's life
  Now wears his crown.

HAMLET: My uncle murdered thee?

GHOST: Brief let me be. Sleeping within my orchard,
  Upon my secure hour thy uncle stole,
  With juice of cursed hebenon in a vial,
  Which in the porches of mine ears he poured.
  Thus was I, sleeping, by a brother's hand
  Of life, of crown, of queen, at once dispatch'd.
  If thou hast nature in thee, bear it not!
  Revenge me, Hamlet. I will be avenged!
  But, howsoever thou pursuest this act,
  Taint not thy mind, nor let thy soul contrive
  Against thy mother aught; leave her to heaven.

Fare thee well at once, my noble son.

(*Fading*) The glow-worm shows the morning to be near.

Adieu! Adieu! Hamlet, remember me!

HAMLET: Remember thee?

Yea, from the table of my memory,

I'll wipe away all trivial fond records,

And thy commandment, all alone, shall live

Within the book and volume of my brain.

The time is out of joint; O cursed spite,

That ever I was born to set right.

MUSIC: *Melancholy theme, in and under.*

NARRATOR: A strolling troupe of actors comes to the castle, and through them, Hamlet perceives a way to discover if the ghost has spoken truly. He arranges with the master of the players to put on a play that will imitate the death of the late king, and by watching the expression on his uncle's face during the play, he will determine his guilt.

HAMLET: Welcome, actors. We'll hear a play tomorrow. Till then, you all will be well bestowed. Tell me, Player Master, can you play "The Murder of Gonzago"?

PLAYER: Ay, my lord.

HAMLET: We'll ha't tomorrow night. You could, for a need, study a speech of some dozen or sixteen lines which I would set down and insert in't, could you not?

PLAYER: Ay, my lord.

HAMLET: Very well, good friend. I'll leave you till tonight.

MUSIC: *Brooding theme, in and under.*

HAMLET: Now I am alone.

O, what a rogue and peasant slave am I!

Is it not monstrous that this player here,

But in a fiction, in a dream of passion,

Could force his soul so to his own conceit
That from her working all his visage wann'd,
Tears in his eyes, distraction in's aspect,
A broken voice, and his whole function suiting
With forms to his conceit? And all for nothing!
What would he do had he the cue for passion
That I have! He would drown the stage with tears,
And cleave the general ear with horrid speech,
Make mad the guilty and appall the free.
Yet I,
A dull and muddy-mettled rascal, peak
And can say nothing! No, not for a king,
Upon whose property and most dear life
A damn'd defeat was made. Am I a coward?
Why, what an ass am I! This is most brave,
That I, the son of a dear father murder'd,
Prompted to my revenge by heaven and hell,
Must, like a girl, unpack my heart with words.
About, my brain! Hmm. I have heard
That guilty creatures sitting at a play
Have by the very cunning of the scene
Been struck so to the soul that presently
They have proclaim'd their malefactions.
Before mine uncle, I shall have these players
Play something like the murder of my father.
I'll observe his looks. If he but blench,
I'll know the course to take. The play's the thing,
Wherein I'll catch the conscience of the king!

MUSIC: *Dramatic theme, in and under.*

NARRATOR: Hamlet has been pretending madness in order
that he might be left alone with his brooding, melancholy thoughts. The king wonders what has caused his

nephew's insanity, and his chamberlain, Polonius, tells him it is unrequited love for Ophelia. The afternoon following the arrival of the company of actors, the king and Polonius hide in a gallery from which they can observe a meeting between Hamlet and Ophelia. Hamlet, unaware that Ophelia has been told to wait for him, is lost in thought.

HAMLET: To be or not to be; that is the question:
Whether 'tis nobler in the mind to suffer
The slings and arrows of outrageous fortune,
Or to take arms against a sea of troubles,
And, by opposing, end them. To die, to sleep;
To sleep? Perchance to dream! Ay, there's the rub!
For in that sleep of death what dreams may come,
When we have shuffled off this mortal coil,
Must give us pause. There's the respect
That makes calamity of so long life.
For who would bear the whips and scorns of time,
The oppressor's wrong, the proud man's contumely,
When he himself might his quietus make
With a bare bodkin? Who would fardels bear,
But that the dread of something after death,
Makes us rather bear those ills we have
Than fly to others that we know not of?
Thus conscience does make cowards of us all.
But stay, what lady's here? Soft you now!
The fair Ophelia? Nymph, in thy orisons
Be all my sins remembered.

OPHELIA (*Fading on*): Good my lord,
How does your honor for this many a day?

HAMLET: I humbly thank you, well, well, well.

OPHELIA: My lord, I have remembrances of yours

That I have longed long to redeliver.

I pray you now receive them.

HAMLET: Are you honest?

OPHELIA: My lord!

HAMLET: Are you fair?

OPHELIA: What means your lordship?

HAMLET: I did love you once.

OPHELIA: Indeed, my lord, you made me believe so.

HAMLET: You should not have believed. I loved you not!

OPHELIA: I was the more deceived!

HAMLET: We are arrant knaves, all. Believe none of us. Get thee to a nunnery, go! Farewell. Or, if thou wilt needs marry, marry a fool. For wise men know well enough what monsters you make of them. (*Fading*) To a nunnery, go, and quickly too! Farewell!

OPHELIA: O heavenly powers, restore him!

O, what a noble mind is here o'erthrown.

The courtier's, soldier's, scholar's, eye, tongue, sword,

The observ'd of all observers, quite, quite down.

And I, of ladies most deject and wretched.

POLONIUS (*Fading on*): How now, Ophelia!

You need not tell us what Lord Hamlet said;

We heard it all. Yet do I believe

The origin and commencement of his grief

Sprung from neglected love, your majesty.

KING: Ay, ay, my good Polonius, so it seems.

POLONIUS: My lord, after the play he gives tonight,

Let his queen-mother all alone entreat him,

And I'll be plac'd, so please you, in the ear

Of all their conference.

KING: It shall be so.

Madness in great ones must not unwatch'd go.

MUSIC: *Turbulent theme, in and under.*

NARRATOR: That night, the unsuspecting king and queen attend a performance by the strolling players. The action of the play, however, so closely parallels the murder of the late king, that Claudius and Gertrude, his queen, become frightened with guilt, and call a stop to the performance. After the play, the queen sends for Hamlet, wishing to speak with him alone in her chamber. Unknown to the young prince, Polonius has conspired with her to hide behind a tapestry and listen.

POLONIUS: Your majesty, I'll silence me e'en here.

Pray you, be round with him.

QUEEN: I shall, Polonius.

HAMLET (*Off mike*): Mother! Mother!

QUEEN: Withdraw, Polonius. I hear him coming.

POLONIUS (*Fading*): Ay, majesty, I'll stand behind this drape.

QUEEN: Fear me not. But soft, here comes the prince.

HAMLET (*Fading on*): Now, mother, what's the matter?

QUEEN: Hamlet, thou hast thy father much offended.

HAMLET: Mother, you have my father much offended.

QUEEN: Come, come! You answer with an idle tongue.

HAMLET: Go, go! You question with a wicked tongue.

Come, come, and sit you down. You shall not budge!

QUEEN: What wilt thou do? Thou wilt not murder me?

Help, help, ho!

POLONIUS (*Off mike*): What ho! Help! Help! Help!

HAMLET: What's this? A rat behind the arras?

SOUND: *Sword being unsheathed.*

HAMLET (*Without pause*): Why then, I'll draw, and kill the listening rat.

POLONIUS (*Gasping, off mike*): O, I am slain!

QUEEN: What hast thou done? What bloody deed is this?

HAMLET: Nay, I know not. Is it the king?

QUEEN: The king!

Nay, 'tis his chamberlain, Polonius!

HAMLET: Thou wretched, rash, intruding fool! Farewell!

I took thee for thy better. Good night, my mother.

I must be cruel only to be kind;

Thus bad begins, and worse remains behind.

MUSIC: *Melancholy theme, in and under.*

NARRATOR: And so Polonius is killed by Hamlet. Upon hearing of her father's death, Ophelia loses her sanity. She asks to visit the queen.

QUEEN: Let her come in.

OPHELIA (*Fading on after a beat*): Where is the beauteous majesty of Denmark?

QUEEN: How now, Ophelia?

OPHELIA (*Singing in her wandering way*): He is dead and gone, lady,

He is dead and gone;

At his head a grass-green turf,

At his heels a stone.

KING (*Fading on*): My lady queen . . .

QUEEN: Alas, look here, my lord.

KING: How do you, pretty lady?

OPHELIA: Well, God 'ild you. They say the owl was a baker's daughter. Lord! We know what we are, but know not what we may be. (*Fading*) God be at your table.

KING: How long hath she been thus?

OPHELIA (*Fading*): I hope all will be well. We must be patient!

KING: Follow her close; give her good watch, I pray you, servant.

SERVANT (*Fading*): Ay, majesty.

KING: Oh, Gertrude, Gertrude. When sorrows come,
They come not single spies, but in battalions.

SERVANT (*Fading on, breathless*): Your majesties, I bid you
save yourselves.
The young Laertes, son of dead Polonius,
That would revenge his loving father's death,
O'erbears your officers. The rabble call him lord.
They cry, "Choose we; Laertes shall be king!"

QUEEN: Oh, this is counter, you false Danish dogs!

SOUND: *Doors being crashed down, off mike.*

KING: The doors are broke!

LAERTES (*Fading on in fury*): O thou vilest king,
Give me my father!

QUEEN: Calmly, good Laertes.

LAERTES: Where's my father?

KING: Dead.

QUEEN: But not by him!

LAERTES: How came he dead? I'll not be juggled with!
Let come what comes, only I'll be revenged
Most thoroughly for my father.

KING: Good Laertes,
That I am guiltless of your father's death,
And am most sensibly in grief for it,
It shall as level to your judgement pierce,
As day does to your eye. Come, go with me;
And as we walk, I shall disclose a plan
By which you shall revenge your father's death.
Come, go, my good Laertes.

MUSIC: *Sinister theme, in and under.*

NARRATOR: With clever words, Claudius turns Laertes' wrath against Hamlet, and persuades him to kill the prince. News that Ophelia, Laertes' sister, in her madness and grief has drowned herself, only confirms his evil intent toward Hamlet. The king works out a plan, whereby a fencing match is to be arranged between Hamlet and Laertes, in which Laertes will fight with a poisoned foil. On the appointed day, the two meet before the assembled court for the preliminaries of shaking hands, choosing weapons, and the duel itself.

KING: Come, Hamlet, take Laertes' hand from me.

HAMLET: Give me your pardon, Laertes. I've done you wrong,

But pardon't, as you are a gentleman.

LAERTES: I do receive your offered love like love,

And will not wrong it.

HAMLET: Give us the foils. Come on.

KING: Give them the foils, young Osric.

LAERTES: This is too heavy. Let me see another.

HAMLET: This likes me well. These foils have all a length?

KING: Ay. Set me the stoups of wine upon that table.

Come, begin. Let the duel begin.

And you, the judges, bear a wary eye.

HAMLET: Come on, sir.

LAERTES: Come, my lord.

SOUND: *Clash of foils.*

HAMLET: One!

LAERTES: No!

HAMLET: Judgement.

HORATIO (*Off mike*): A hit, a very palpable hit!

LAERTES: Well; again.

KING: Stay; give me drink. Hamlet, here's to thy health.

NARRATOR (*In close*): The king holds up a cup of poisoned wine, and, after pretending to drink from it himself, offers the cup to Hamlet.

KING: Give him the cup.

HAMLET: I'll play this bout first; set it by awhile.
Come!

QUEEN: I drink this wine to thy good fortune, Hamlet.

HAMLET: Good madam!

KING: Gertrude, do not drink!

QUEEN: I will, my lord! I pray you pardon me.

KING (*As an aside*): It is the poisoned cup! It is too late!

HAMLET: Come, for the third! Laertes, you but dally.

LAERTES: Say you so? Come on. Have at you—now!

SOUND: *Violent clash of foils.*

NARRATOR: Laertes, abandoning all defense, rushes in upon Hamlet and wounds him. Each seizes the other's wrist, and in the scuffle, they exchange weapons. Hamlet, unaware that he is holding a poisoned foil—indeed that he has been stabbed by it—wounds Laertes.

KING: Part them! They are incens'd!

HORATIO: They bleed on both sides. How is it, Hamlet?

KING: How is it, Laertes?

LAERTES: Why, I am justly killed with mine own treachery.

HAMLET: How does the queen?

KING: She swoons to see them bleed.

QUEEN (*Gasping*): No, no, the drink! The drink! O my dear Hamlet!
The drink! The drink! I am poisoned.

HAMLET: O villainy! Treachery! Seek it out!

LAERTES: It is here, Hamlet. Hamlet, thou art slain.
In thee there is not half an hour of life.

The treacherous instrument is in thy hand,
Unbated and envenom'd. The foul practice
Hath turned itself on me. Thy mother's poisoned.
I can no more. The king, the king's to blame!

HAMLET: The point envenom'd too! Then, venom, kill!
Here, thou murderous, damned uncle Claudius.
Follow my mother to an early death.
Thus, with this poisoned foil, I murder thee.

LAERTES: Exchange forgiveness with me, noble Hamlet.
Mine and my father's death come not upon thee,
Nor thine—on me . . . (*Gasps*)

HAMLET: Heaven make thee free of it! I follow thee.
Horatio, I am dead. Thou only, livest.
Report my cause aright to the unsatisfied.
O God, Horatio, what a wounded name,
Things standing thus unknown, shall live behind me!
If thou didst ever hold me in thy heart,
Absent thee from felicity awhile,
And in this harsh world draw thy breath in pain,
To tell my story. O, I die, Horatio!
The potent poison quite o'ercrows my spirit.
The rest is . . . silence.

HORATIO: Now cracks a noble heart! Goodnight, sweet
prince,
And flights of angels sing thee to thy rest.

MUSIC: *Tragic theme, full to finish.*

THE END

King Lear

Characters

KING LEAR
GONERIL
CORDELIA
REGAN
KING OF FRANCE

LEAR'S FOOL
A DOCTOR
A CAPTAIN
NARRATOR

NARRATOR: The majesty, the poetry and the passion with which man can suffer for his own follies have never been portrayed as magnificently, as poignantly as in *King Lear,* the tragedy of a father's inability to recognize true devotion in a child.

SOUND: *Fanfare.*

NARRATOR: Tired of the pomp, ceremony and obligations of his position, and longing for a life of rest and quiet, Lear, elderly King of Britain, determines to divide his kingdom among his three daughters, each to earn her portion by a declaration of love for the King. His first two daughters, Goneril and Regan, are eager for large portions of the kingdom, although they have little love for their father. The youngest, Cordelia, wants only to make her father happy. As the play begins, the King

152

has assembled his court for the division of the kingdom.
Before him stand his eldest daughter, Goneril, and her
husband, the Duke of Albany; the second daughter,
Regan, and her husband, the Duke of Cornwall; and
the youngest child, Cordelia, with her two suitors, the
Duke of Burgundy and the King of France.

SOUND: *Fanfare.*

LEAR: Know that we have divided
    In three our kingdom; and 'tis our fast intent
    To shake all cares and business from our age,
    Conferring them on younger strengths, while we
    Unburden'd crawl toward death. Our son of Cornwall,
    And you, our no less loving son of Albany,
    We have this hour a constant will to publish
    Our daughters' several dowers, that future strife
    May be prevented now. The Princes, France and Bur-
      gundy,
    Great rivals in our youngest daughter's love,
    Long in our court have made their amorous sojourn,
    And here are to be answer'd. Tell me, my daughters—
    Since now we will divest us both of rule,
    Interest of territory, cares of state—
    Which of you shall we say doth love us most,
    That we our largest bounty may extend
    Where nature doth with merit challenge? Goneril,
    Our eldest-born, speak first.

GONERIL: Sir, I do love you more than words can wield
    the matter;
    Dearer than eye-sight, space and liberty:
    Beyond what can be valued, rich or rare;
    No less than life, with grace, health, beauty, honor;
    As much as child e'er loved, or father found;

Beyond all manner of so much I love you.

CORDELIA (*In close, as an aside*): What shall Cordelia
speak? Love and be silent.

LEAR: Of all these bounds, my eldest daughter Goneril,
With shadowy forest and with champains rich'd,
We make thee lady. To thine and Albany's issues
Be this perpetual. What says our second daughter,
Our dearest Regan, wife of Cornwall? Speak.

REGAN: I am made of that self metal as my sister,
And prize me at her worth. In my true heart,
I find she names my very deed of love;
Only she comes too short, that I profess
Myself an enemy to all other joys
And find I am alone felicitate
In your dear Highness' love.

CORDELIA (*In close, as an aside*): Then poor Cordelia!
And yet not so; since, I am sure, my love's
More ponderous than my tongue.

LEAR: To thee and thine hereditary ever
This third of our fair kingdom. Now, our joy,
Although our last and least, to whose young love
The vines of France and milk of Burgundy
Strive to be interest, what can you say to draw
A third more opulent than your sisters? Speak.

CORDELIA: Nothing, my lord.

LEAR: Nothing will come of nothing! Speak again!

CORDELIA: Unhappy that I am, I cannot heave
My heart into my mouth. I love your Majesty
According to my bond; nor more nor less.

LEAR: How, how, Cordelia! Mend your speech a little,
Lest you may mar your fortunes.

CORDELIA: Good my lord,

You have begot me, bred me, lov'd me: I
Return those duties back as are right fit;
Obey you, love you, and most honor you.
Why have my sisters husbands if they say
They love you all? Haply, when I shall wed,
That lord whose hand must take my plight shall carry
Half my love with him, half my care and duty.

LEAR: But goes thy heart with this?

CORDELIA: Ay, my good lord.

LEAR: So young, and so untender?

CORDELIA: So young, my lord, and true.

LEAR: Let it be so; thy truth, then, be thy dower!
Here I disclaim all my paternal care,
And as a stranger to my heart and me
Hold thee from this for ever, my sometime daughter!
Hence and avoid my sight! Call France! Call Burgundy!

KING OF FRANCE: Here's France and Burgundy, my noble
lord.

LEAR: Sirs, there she stands; my youngest, least-lov'd daugh-
ter;
If aught within that little-seeming substance,
Or all of it, with your displeasure piec'd,
And nothing more, may like either of you,
Take her or leave her.

FRANCE: This is most strange,
That she, that even but now was your best object,
Most best, most dearest, should in this trice of time
Be fall'n from affection.

CORDELIA: I yet beseech your Majesty,
That you make known it is no vicious blot
That hath deprived me of your grace and favor;
But even for want of that for which I am richer,

A still-soliciting eye and such a tongue
That I am glad I have not, though not to have it
Hath lost me in your liking.

LEAR: Better thou
Hadst not been born than not to have pleased me better.

FRANCE: Fairest Cordelia, that art most rich being poor,
Most choice forsaken, and most lov'd despis'd!
Thee and thy virtues here I seize upon,
Be it lawful I take up what's cast away.
Thy dowerless daughter, king, thrown to my chance,
Is queen of us, of ours, and our fair France.
Bid them farewell, Cordelia, though unkind;
Thou losest here, a better where to find.

LEAR: Thou hast her, France. Let her be thine; for we
Have no such daughter, nor ever shall see
That face of hers again. Therefore be gone
Without our grace, our love, our benison.

MUSIC: *Cold, royal theme, in and under.*

NARRATOR: And so the penniless Cordelia becomes Queen
of France. Knowing that their father's favorite had always been their younger sister, Cordelia, the two older
girls, Goneril and Regan, discuss their father's sudden
change of heart. As he is to spend alternate months of
the year with each of them, they resolve to watch him
closely, and give him as little freedom as possible.

GONERIL: Sister, it is not little I have to say of what most
nearly appertains to us both. I think our father will
hence tonight.

REGAN: That's most certain, and with you; next month
with us.

GONERIL: You see how full of changes his age is. He always

loved our sister most; and with what poor judgement he hath cast her off appears too grossly.

REGAN: 'Tis the infirmity of his age; yet he hath ever but slenderly known himself.

GONERIL: Then must we look to receive from his age not alone the imperfections of long-engrafted condition, but therewithal the unruly waywardness that infirm and choleric years bring with them.

REGAN: Such unconstant starts are we like to have from him as this of Cordelia's banishment.

GONERIL: Pray you, let's hit together; if our father carry authority with such dispositions as he bears, this last surrender of his will but offend us.

REGAN: We shall further think on't.

GONERIL: We must do something, and i' th' heat.

MUSIC: *Evil theme, in and under.*

NARRATOR: Once mistress over half of Lear's kingdom, Goneril resolves to order her father about. Displeased that he keeps a company of one hundred soldiers, in addition to his Fool, who is the old king's constant companion, Goneril decides that fifty are enough, and goes to her father who sits alone with his old friend, the Fool, to announce her decision, her face set in firm determination.

LEAR: How now, daughter! What makes that frontlet on? Methinks you are too much of late i' th' frown.

FOOL: Thou wast a pretty fellow when thou hadst no need to care for her frowning; now thou art an O without a figure. I am better than thou art now; I am a Fool, thou art nothing.

GONERIL: Not only, sir, this your all-licensed Fool,

But other of your insolent retinue
Do hourly carp and quarrel, breaking forth
In rank and not-to-be-endured riots.

LEAR: Are you our daughter?

GONERIL: Come, sir,
I would you would make use of that good wisdom,
Whereof I know you are fraught, and put away
These dispositions, which of late transport you
From what you rightly are.

LEAR: Doth any here know me? This is not Lear.
Doth Lear walk thus? Speak thus? Where are his eyes?
Who is it that can tell me who I am?

FOOL: Lear's shadow.

LEAR: I would learn that; for, by the marks of sovereignty,
knowledge, and reason, I should be false persuaded I
had daughters.

GONERIL: This admiration, sir, is much o' th' savor
Of other your new pranks. I do beseech you
As you are old and reverend, you should be wise.
Here do you keep a hundred knights and squires;
Men so disorder'd, so debosh'd and bold,
That this our court, infected with their manners,
Shows like a riotous inn. Be then desir'd
A little to disquantity your train.

LEAR (*Furiously*): Darkness and devils!
Saddle my horses; call my train together!
Detested kite, I'll not trouble thee.
Yet have I left a daughter. Prepare my horses!
Ingratitude, thou marble-hearted fiend,
More hideous when thou show'st thee in a child
Than the sea-monster! O, most small fault,
How ugly didst thou in Cordelia show!

Which wrench'd my nature, drew from my heart all
love,
And added to the gall. O, Lear, Lear, Lear!
How sharper than a serpent's tooth it is
To have a thankless child! Away, away!
Let it be so: I have another daughter,
(Fading) Who, I am sure, is kind and comfortable.

GONERIL *(Coldly)*: You, sir, more knave than fool, after
your master.

FOOL *(Fading, calling)*: Nuncle Lear, nuncle Lear! Tarry
and take the Fool with thee!

MUSIC: *Unhappy theme, in and under.*

NARRATOR: Little realizing that Regan is even less anxious
to have her father than Goneril, Lear sets out for her
castle with his Fool and his retinue. His daughter,
Regan, meets him outside the castle gates.

REGAN: I am glad to see your Highness.

LEAR: Regan, I think you are; I know what reason
I have to think so. Beloved Regan,
Thy sister's naught. O Regan, she hath tied
Sharp-tooth'd unkindness, like a vulture, here.

REGAN: I pray you, sir, take patience.

LEAR: How is that?

REGAN: I cannot think my sister in the least
Would fail her obligation. If, sir, perchance
She have restrain'd the riots of your followers,
'Tis on such ground, and to such wholesome end
As clears her from all blame.

LEAR: My curses on her!

REGAN: O, sir, you are old;
Nature in you stands on the very verge
Of her confine. You should be ruled and led

By some discretion. Therefore, I pray you,
That to our sister you do make return;
Say you have wrong'd her, sir.

LEAR: Ask her forgiveness?
Never, Regan. She hath abated my train;
Look'd black upon me; struck me with her tongue.
You nimble lightnings, dart your blinding flames
Into her scornful eyes! Infect her beauty
To fall and blast her pride!

REGAN: O, the blest gods! So will you wish on me,
When the rash mood is on.

LEAR: No, Regan, thou shalt never have my curse.
Thy half o' the kingdom hast thou not forgot,
Wherein I thee endow'd.

SOUND: *Fanfare.*

LEAR: What trumpet's that?

REGAN: I know't; my sister's. This approves her letter,
That she would soon be here. 'Tis Goneril.
Welcome, sister Goneril, to my house.

LEAR: O, Regan, wilt thou take her by the hand?

GONERIL (*Fading on*): Why not by the hand, sir? How
have I offended?

REGAN: I pray you, father, being weak, seem so.
If, till the expiration of your month,
You will return and sojourn with my sister,
Dismissing half your train, come then to me.

LEAR: Return to her and fifty men dismiss'd?
No, rather I abjure all roofs, and choose
To wage against the enmity o' the air;
Why, the hot-blooded France, that dowerless took
Our youngest born, I could as well be brought
To knee his throne, and squire-like, pension beg

To keep base life afoot. Return with her?
Persuade me rather to be slave and sumpter!

GONERIL: At your choice, sir.

LEAR: I prithee, daughter, do not make me mad!
You heavens, give me that patience, patience I need!
You see me here, you gods, a poor old man,
As full of grief as age; wretched in both!
If it be you that stirs these daughters' hearts
Against their father, fool me not so much
To bear it tamely; touch me with noble anger,
And let not women's weapons, water drops,
Stain my man's cheeks! No, I'll not weep.
I have full cause of weeping; but this heart
Shall break into a hundred thousand flaws,
Or ere I'll weep. O, Fool! I shall go mad!

SOUND: *Thunder, lightning, and rain.*

NARRATOR: And so, homeless and friendless, Lear makes
his way into the dark, stormy night, accompanied only
by his faithful Fool.

SOUND: *Storm noises up, then softly to background.*

LEAR: Blow, winds, and crack your cheeks! Rage! Blow!
You cataracts and hurricanoes, spout!
You sulph'rous and thought-executing fires,
Vaunt-couriers to oak-cleaving thunderbolts,
Singe my white head! And thou, all-shaking thunder,
Strike flat the thick rotundity o' the world!

FOOL: O, nuncle, court holy-water in a dry house is better
than this rain water out o' door. Good nuncle, in, and
ask thy daughters' blessing. Here's a night pities neither
wise man nor fool.

LEAR: Rumble thy bellyful! Spit, fire! Spout, rain!
Nor rain, wind, thunder, fire, are my daughters.

I tax not you, you elements, with unkindness,
I never gave you kingdom, call'd you children;
You owe me no subscription: then let fall
Your horrible pleasure. Here I stand, your slave,
A poor, infirm, weak and despis'd old man;
But yet I call you servile ministers,
That will with two pernicious daughters join
Your high-engender'd battles 'gainst a head
So old and white as this. Oh! Oh! 'Tis foul!

SOUND: *Storm noises up, segue with*

MUSIC: *Unhappy theme, in and under.*

NARRATOR: Gradually, the wandering, miserable King loses his mind. One night, in his madness, he holds a mock trial at which he arraigns his daughters.

LEAR: Arraign her first; 'tis Goneril. I here take my oath before this honorable assembly, she kicked the poor king her father.

FOOL: Come hither, mistress. Is your name Goneril?

LEAR: She cannot deny it!

FOOL: Cry you mercy, I took you for a joint-stool.

LEAR: And here's another, whose warp'd looks proclaim
What store her heart is made on. Stop her there!
Arms, arms, sword, fire! Corruption in the place!
False justicer, why hast thou let her scape?
The little dogs and all,
Tray, Blanch, and Sweetheart, see, they bark at me.

FOOL: Avaunt, you curs!

LEAR: Then let them anatomize Regan; see what breeds about her heart. Is there any cause in nature that make these hard hearts?

FOOL: Now, good my lord, lie here and rest awhile.

LEAR: Make no noise, make no noise; draw the curtains; so, so, so. We'll go to supper i' th' morning; so, so, so.

FOOL: And I'll go to bed at noon.

MUSIC: *Melancholy theme, in and under.*

NARRATOR: Meanwhile, Albany and Cornwall, husbands of Goneril and Regan, have quarreled over the division of the kingdom, and are preparing for battle. Hearing of their dispute, the French army makes preparation to attack, and lands on the British coast, near Dover, where Cordelia, now Queen of France, finds her father wandering over the countryside, his mind distracted, garlands of flowers in his hair. She orders him taken to her tent, where the court physician attends him.

CORDELIA: How does the King, good doctor?

DOCTOR (*Fading on*): Madam, sleeps still.

CORDELIA: O you kind gods,
    Cure this great breach in his abused nature!
    Th' untuned and jarring senses, O, wind up
    Of this child-changed father!

DOCTOR: So please your Majesty
    That we may wake the King? He hath slept long.

CORDELIA: Be govern'd by your knowledge, and proceed
    I' th' sway of your own will.

DOCTOR (*Calling off mike*): Bring forth the sleeping King!
    (*In again*)
    Good madam, be by when we do awake him.

CORDELIA: Very well.

DOCTOR: Please you draw nearer.

CORDELIA: O my dear father! Restoration hang
    Thy medicine on my lips; and let this kiss
    Repair those violent harms that my two sisters

Have in thy reverence made! Was this a face
To be oppos'd against the warring winds?
To stand against the deep dread-bolted thunder?
'Tis wonder that thy life and wits at once
Had not concluded all. He wakes; speak to him.

DOCTOR: Madam, do you; 'tis fittest.

CORDELIA: How does my royal lord? How fares your
Majesty?

LEAR: You do me wrong to take me out o' the grave.
Thou art a soul in bliss; but I am bound
Upon a wheel of fire, that mine own tears
Do scald like molten lead.

CORDELIA: Sir, do you know me?

LEAR: You are a spirit, I know; when did you die?

CORDELIA: Still, still, far wide!

DOCTOR (*Slightly off mike*): He's scarce awake; let him
alone awhile.

LEAR: Where have I been? Where am I? Fair daylight?
I will not swear these are my hands. Let's see;
I feel this pin prick. Would I were assured
Of my condition.

CORDELIA: O, look upon me, sir,
And hold your hand in benediction o'er me.
No, sir, you must not kneel.

LEAR: Pray, do not mock me.
I am a very foolish fond old man.
Fourscore and upward, not an hour more or less;
And, to deal plainly,
I fear I am not in my perfect mind.
Methinks I should know you and know this man;
Yet I am doubtful; for I am mainly ignorant

What place this is, and all the skill I have
Remembers not these garments; nor I know not
Where I did lodge last night. Do not laugh at me;
For, as I am a man, I think this lady
To be my child Cordelia.

CORDELIA: And so I am, I am.

LEAR: Be your tears wet? Yes, faith. I pray, weep not.
If you have poison for me, I will drink it.
I know you do not love me; for your sisters
Have, as I do remember, done me wrong:
You have some cause, they have not.

CORDELIA: No cause, no cause.

LEAR: Am I in France?

CORDELIA: In your own kingdom, sir.

LEAR: Do not abuse me.

DOCTOR: Be comforted, good madam; the great rage,
You see, is kill'd in him: and yet it is danger
To make him even o'er the time he has lost.
Desire him to go in; trouble him no more
'Til further settling.

CORDELIA: Will 't please your Highness walk?

LEAR: You must bear with me.
Pray you now, forget and forgive; I am old and foolish.

MUSIC: *Heavy theme, in and under.*

NARRATOR: With her father restored to her in safety,
Cordelia believes all her unhappiness at an end. In the
battles which follow, however, Goneril and Regan are
killed, and Cordelia and the old King himself are taken
prisoners by the enemy.

CAPTAIN: Some officers take them away!

CORDELIA: We are not the first

Who, with best meaning, have incurr'd the worst.
For thee, oppressed king, am I cast down;
Myself could else out-frown false fortune's frown.

LEAR: Come, let's away to prison.
We two alone will sing like birds i' the cage.
When thou dost ask my blessing, I'll kneel down
And ask of thee forgiveness. So we'll live,
And pray, and sing, and tell old tales, and laugh
At gilded butterflies, and hear poor rogues
Talk of court news; and we'll talk with them too,
Who loses and who wins; who's in, who's out.

CAPTAIN (*Off mike*): Take them away.

LEAR: Upon such sacrifices, my Cordelia,
The gods themselves throw incense. Have I caught thee?
He that parts us shall bring a brand from heaven,
And fire us hence like foxes. Wipe thine eye;
The good-years shall devour them, flesh and fell,
Ere they shall make us weep. We'll see 'em starv'd first.
Come.

MUSIC: *Melancholy theme, in and under.*

NARRATOR: Once taken, Cordelia, as Queen of France, is
ordered killed. King Lear is brought to her cell just in
time to see her hanged. Seizing a guard's knife, he kills
her murderer, and cuts down the dying body of his
youngest child. Tenderly holding her in his arms, he
takes a last farewell of her.

LEAR: Howl, howl, howl! O, you men of stone!
Had I your tongues and eyes, I'd use them so
That heaven's vault should crack. She's gone forever!
I know when one is dead, and when one lives;
She's dead as earth. Lend me a looking glass;
If that her breath will mist or stain the stone,

Why then she lives. She lives! If it be so,
It is a chance which does redeem all sorrows
That ever I have felt. No, no, she's dead.
A plague upon you, murderous traitors all!
I might have sav'd her; now she's gone for ever!
Cordelia, Cordelia! Stay a little! Ha!
What is't thou say'st? Her voice was ever soft,
Gentle and low, an excellent thing in woman.
I kill'd the slave that was a-hanging thee.
I have seen the day, with my good biting falchion
I would have made him skip. I am old now.
And my poor fool is hang'd! No, no, no life!
Why should a dog, a horse, a rat have life,
And thou no breath at all? Thou'lt come no more,
Never, never, never, never, never!
Pray you, undo this button. Thank you, sir.

MUSIC: *Tragic theme, sneak into background under following.*

LEAR: Do you see this? Look on her, look, her lips,
   Look there . . . look there . . . (*Sighs*)

NARRATOR: So, on the stone floor of his prison, Lear, King of Britain, now old and insane, the body of his lifeless child, Cordelia, in his arms, dies . . . unnoticed . . . unwanted . . . unloved.

MUSIC: *Full to finish.*

THE END

Macbeth

Characters

THREE WITCHES

MACBETH

BANQUO

ROSS, *a noble*

LADY MACBETH

A MESSENGER

MACDUFF, *a noble*

LENNOX, *a noble*

THREE APPARITIONS

TWO LORDS

DOCTOR

NURSE

NARRATOR

NARRATOR: Against the chill and stormy background of eleventh century Scotland, William Shakespeare unfolded a violent and bloody story of death, crime and punishment. In a time when witches and evil spirits roamed the earth, making their foul predictions, there lived a soldier of great courage, great strength, and great ambition—Macbeth.

SOUND: *Wind, rain and thunder.*

MUSIC: *Eerie theme, in and under.*

1ST WITCH (*A shrill, cackling voice*): When shall we three meet again?

In thunder, lightning, or in rain?

2ND WITCH: When the hurlyburly's done,
When the battle's lost and won.

3RD WITCH: That will be ere the set of sun.

1ST WITCH: Where the place?

2ND WITCH: Upon the heath.

3RD WITCH: There to meet with Macbeth.

ALL (*In unison, chanting weirdly*): Fair is foul and foul
is fair.
Hover through the fog and filthy air.

SOUND: *A drum slightly off mike.*

3RD WITCH: A drum! A drum! Macbeth doth come.

WITCHES (*Chanting in unison*): The weird sisters, hand
in hand,
Posters of the sea and land,
Thus do go about, about,
Thrice to thine, thrice to mine,
Thrice again to make up nine.
Peace! The charm's wound up!

MACBETH (*A mature, vigorous voice, fading on*): So foul
and fair a day I have not seen.

BANQUO (*Of the same age*): What are these, most valorous
Macbeth,
So withered and so wild in their attire?
They look not like inhabitants of earth
And yet are on it. Live you? You should be women,
And yet your beards forbid me to interpret
That you are so.

MACBETH (*Challenging*): Speak, if you can. What are you?

1ST WITCH: All hail, Macbeth! Thane of Glamis.

2ND WITCH: All hail, Macbeth, Thane of Cawdor.

3RD WITCH: All hail, Macbeth, that shalt be king hereafter!

MACBETH (*Astonished*): What! Banquo, did you hear?

BANQUO: Macbeth, why do you start, and seem to fear
Things that do sound so fair? My noble partner
You greet, oh women wild, with great prediction
Of noble having and of royal hope,
That he seems rapt withal. To me you speak not.
If you can look into the seeds of time
And say which grain will grow and which will not,
Speak then to me, who neither beg nor fear
Your favors nor your hate.

WITCHES (*In unison*): Hail, Banquo!

1ST WITCH: Lesser than Macbeth, and greater.

2ND WITCH: Not so happy, yet much happier.

3RD WITCH: Thou shalt get kings, though thou be none.
So all hail, Macbeth and Banquo.

WITCHES (*In unison*): Banquo and Macbeth, all hail.

MACBETH: Stay, you imperfect speakers, tell me more!
By my father's death I know I am Thane of Glamis;
But how of Cawdor? The Thane of Cawdor lives,
A prosperous gentleman; and to be king
Stands not within the prospect of belief,
No more than to be Cawdor. Say from whence
You owe this strange intelligence? Or why
Upon this blasted heath you stop our way
With such prophetic greeting? Speak, I charge you!

WITCHES (*Hissing, fading off*): Ssssss!

SOUND: *A clap of thunder.*

BANQUO: Whither are they vanished?

MACBETH: Into the air, Banquo. Would they had stayed!

BANQUO: Were such things really here, or have we eaten
On the insane root that takes the reason prisoner?

MACBETH (*Wonderingly*). Your children, Banquo, shall
  be kings.
BANQUO: You shall be king.
MACBETH: And Thane of Cawdor too.
  Went it not so?
BANQUO: To the self-same tune and words.
  But look you. Who's here?
MACBETH: It is our kinsman, Ross.
ROSS (*Fading on*): Hail, Banquo and Macbeth.
MACBETH *and* BANQUO: Hail, Ross.
ROSS: The king hath happily received, Macbeth,
  The news of thy success in recent battle.
  Everyone did highly bear to Duncan
  Thy praises in his kingdom's great defense,
  And poured them down before him.
MACBETH: Thou art too kind.
ROSS: And in reward, he bade me, from him, call thee
  Thane of Cawdor.
BANQUO (*Softly*): What, can the devil speak true?
MACBETH (*Bewildered*): The Thane of Cawdor lives. Why
    do you dress me
  In borrowed robes?
ROSS: Who was the Thane lives yet,
  But under heavy judgement bears that life
  Which he deserves to lose. Treasons capital,
  Confessed and proved, have overthrown him.
MACBETH (*Softly*): Glamis and Cawdor too! The greatest
    is behind.
  (*Aloud*) Thanks, cousin, for your pains. (*Softly, ur-
    gently*) Banquo, Banquo,
  Do you not hope your children shall be kings,

When those that gave the Thane of Cawdor to me
Promised no less to them?

BANQUO: Oftentimes, to win us to our harm,
The instruments of darkness tell us truths,
Win us with honest trifles to betray us
In deepest consequence.

MACBETH (*With conviction*): Come what come may,
Time and the hour runs through the roughest day.

MUSIC: *Dramatic theme, in and under.*

NARRATOR: Thus the prediction of the witches, which had seemed so incredible, has already begun to come true. Macbeth, amazed and shaken, writes of the wonderful happenings to his lady, and sends the letter by messenger ahead of his own arrival.

LADY MACBETH (*Mature voice, reading*): "They met me in the day of success; and I have learned by the perfectest report that they have more in them than mortal knowledge. When I burned in desire to question them further, they made themselves air, into which they vanished. Whiles I stood rapt with the wonder of it, came missives from the King, who all-hailed me 'Thane of Cawdor,' by which title these weird sisters had saluted me, and referred me to the coming on of time with 'Hail, king that shalt be!' This have I thought good to deliver thee, my dearest partner of greatness. Lay it to thy heart, and farewell."

(*After a pause, determinedly*) Glamis thou art, and Cawdor, and shalt be
What thou art promised. Yet do I fear thy nature.
It is too full of the milk of human kindness
To catch the nearest way. What thou wouldst highly,
That wouldst thou holily. Hie thee hither, then,

That I may pour my spirits in thine ear
And chastise with the valor of my tongue
All that impedes thee from the golden round
Which fate doth seem to have thee crowned withal.

MESSENGER (*Fading on*): My lady.

LADY MACBETH: What is your tidings?

MESSENGER: The King comes here tonight.

LADY MACBETH (*Angrily*): Thou'rt mad to say it!
Thy master would have informed for preparation.

MESSENGER: So please you, it is true. Our Thane is coming.
One of my fellows had the speed of him,
Who, almost dead for breath, had scarcely more
Than would make up his message.

LADY MACBETH: Give him tending;
He brings great news. (*In close*) The raven himself is hoarse
That croaks the fatal entrance of King Duncan
Under my battlements. Come, you spirits
That tend on mortal thoughts; come fill me
From the crown to the toe, top-full of direst cruelty!
Make thick my blood! Come, come, oh cruel night,
And pall thee in the dunnest smoke of hell
That my keen knife see not the wound it makes,
Nor heaven peep through the blanket of the dark
To cry "Hold, hold!"

MACBETH (*Fading on*): My wife!

LADY MACBETH (*Proudly*): Great Glamis! Worthy Cawdor!
Greater than both by the all-hail hereafter!

MACBETH: My dearest love, Duncan comes here tonight.

LADY MACBETH: And when goes hence?

MACBETH: Tomorrow . . . as he purposes.

LADY MACBETH (*Determinedly*): O, never shall sun that morrow see.

Your face, my Thane, is as a book where men
May read strange matters. Look like the innocent flower,
But be the serpent under it. He that's coming
Must be provided for; and you shall put
This night's great business into my dispatch,
Which shall to all our nights and days to come
Give solely sovereign sway and masterdom.

MACBETH: We will speak further.

LADY MACBETH: Only look up clear.

To alter favor ever is to fear.

(*Ominously*) Leave all the rest to me.

MUSIC: *A forbidding theme, in and under.*

NARRATOR: With King Duncan under their own roof, Lady Macbeth plots his murder, in order to complete the witches' prophecy. Macbeth, however, who is to perform the bloody deed that night, suffers from pangs of conscience.

MACBETH (*Deep in thought*): If it were done, when 'tis done, then 'twere well

It were done quickly. That but this blow
Might be the be-all and the end-all here,
But here, upon this bank and shoal of time,
We'd jump the life to come. But in these cases
We still have judgement here, that we but teach
Bloody instructions, which, being taught, return
To plague the inventor.

LADY MACBETH (*Off mike*): Husband?

MACBETH: How now? What news?

LADY MACBETH (*Fading on*): He has almost supped.

MACBETH: Hath he asked for me?

LADY MACBETH: Know you not he has?

MACBETH: We will proceed no further in this business.
He hath honored me of late, which honors
Would be worn now in their newest gloss,
Not cast aside so soon.

LADY MACBETH: Was the hope drunk wherein you dressed
yourself?
Hath it slept since? And wakes it now to look
So green and pale at what it did so freely,
Letting "I dare not" wait upon "I would,"
Like the poor cat i' the adage?

MACBETH: Prithee, peace!
I dare do all that may become a man.
Who dares do more is none.

LADY MACBETH: What beast was it then
That made you break this enterprise to me?

MACBETH: If we should fail?

LADY MACBETH: We fail!
But screw your courage to the sticking place
And we'll not fail! When Duncan is asleep—
And he is weary—his two chamberlains
Will I with wine and wassail so convince,
That memory and the receipt of reason
Shall be a limbeck only. Then, Macbeth,
What cannot you and I perform upon
The unguarded Duncan?

MACBETH: Will it not be received when we have marked
With blood those sleepy two of his own chamber,
And used their very daggers for the deed,
That they have done it?

LADY MACBETH: Who dares receive it other,
As we shall make our griefs and clamor roar
Upon his death?

MACBETH: Then I am settled, and bend up
Each corporal agent to this terrible feat.
Away, and mock the time with fairest show;
False face must hide what the false heart doth know.

MUSIC: *Forbidding theme, in and under.*

NARRATOR: That night, while all the castle sleeps, Macbeth steals upstairs to the king's chamber to perform the murder. Meanwhile, Lady Macbeth waits anxiously in the great hall for her husband to return.

LADY MACBETH: That which hath made them drunk hath made me bold.
Hark! Peace! He is about it!
The doors are open, and the sleepy grooms
Do mock their charge with snores. I have drugged their possets.

MACBETH (*Off mike*): Who's there? What, ho?

LADY MACBETH (*Distressed*): Alack, I am afraid they have awaked
And 'tis not done! The attempt and not the deed
Confounds us. Hark! Had he not resembled
My father as he slept, I had done't!

MACBETH (*Fading on*): I have done the deed. His blood is on my hands.
Methought I heard a voice cry "Sleep no more.
Macbeth doth murder sleep." The innocent sleep,
Sleep that knits up the ravell'd sleave of care,
The death of each day's life, sore labor's bath,
Balm of hurt minds, great nature's second course,
Chief nourisher in life's feast—

LADY MACBETH: What mean you, my lord?

MACBETH: Still it cried "Sleep no more!" To all the house:
"Glamis hath murdered sleep, and therefore Cawdor
Shall sleep no more: Macbeth shall sleep no more."

LADY MACBETH: Who was it that thus cried? Why, worthy
husband,
You do unbend your noble strength to think
So brainsickly of things. Go get some water,
And wash this filthy witness from your hands.
(*Appalled*) Why did you bring these daggers from the
place?
They must lie there! Carry them back and smear
The sleepy grooms with blood.

MACBETH: I'll go no more.
I am afraid to think what I have done;
I dare not look at it again.

LADY MACBETH (*Disgusted*): Infirm of purpose!
Give me the daggers! The sleeping and the dead
Are but as pictures. (*Fading*) 'Tis the eye of childhood
That fears a painted devil.

SOUND: *Knocking off mike.*

MACBETH (*Terrified*): Whence is that knocking?
How is't with me, when every noise appalls me?

LADY MACBETH (*Fading on*): My hands are of your color
now, but I shame
To wear a heart so white.

SOUND: *Knocking off mike.*

LADY MACBETH (*Urgently*): I hear a knocking
At the south entry. Retire we to our chamber!
A little water clears us of this deed.
How easy is it then!

SOUND: *Knocking, loud and insistent.*

MACBETH: Wake Duncan with thy knocking! I would thou couldst!

MUSIC: *Foreboding theme, in and under.*

NARRATOR: Knocking at the gate are Macduff and Lennox, kinsmen of Macbeth, who had been ordered by the king to come and wake him early in the day. A porter admits them to the castle.

SOUND: *Knocking, closer to mike.*

MESSENGER (*Fading on*): Anon, anon! I come! Prithee patience!

SOUND: *Door opening.*

MACDUFF (*Fading on*): Was it so late, friend, ere you went to bed,
That you do lie so late?

MESSENGER: Faith, sir, we were carousing till the second cock.

MACDUFF: Is thy master stirring?
Ah, our knocking has awaked him; here he comes.

LENNOX: Aye. Good morrow, noble sir.

MACBETH (*Fading on*): Good morrow to you both, Macduff and Lennox.

MACDUFF: Is the king stirring, worthy Thane?

MACBETH: Not yet.

MACDUFF: He did command me to call timely on him.

MACBETH: I'll bring you to him. This is the door.

MACDUFF (*Fading*): I'll make so bold to call, for 'tis my limited service.

LENNOX: Goes the king hence today?

MACBETH: He does, good Lennox. (*Catching himself*) He did appoint so.

MACDUFF (*Shouting off mike, fading on*): O horror, horror, horror!

MACBETH *and* LENNOX: What's the matter?

MACDUFF *(Wildly)*: His Majesty is murdered! Go and see!
Awake! Awake! Ring the alarum bell!
Murder and treason! Malcolm! Banquo! Awake!
Ring the bell!

SOUND: *Alarum bell being rung off mike. Ad lib of crowd
fading on.*

LADY MACBETH *(Fading on)*: What's the business
That such a hideous trumpet calls to parley
The sleepers of the house? Speak, speak!

MACDUFF: O gentle lady,
The repetition in a woman's ear
Would murder as it fell. O Banquo, Banquo,
Our royal master's murdered!

LADY MACBETH *(Weakly)*: Woe, alas! What, in our house?
Help me hence, ho!

BANQUO: Look to the lady! Now let us meet to question
This most bloody piece of work to know it further.
In the great hand of God I stand, and thence
Against the undivulged pretence I fight
Of treasonous malice.

MACDUFF: And so do I.

ALL *(In unison)*: So all!

BANQUO: Let's briefly put on manly readiness,
And meet in the hall together.

MUSIC: *Militant theme, in and under.*

NARRATOR: News of the murder spreads quickly. Macduff
encounters Ross, and discusses the latest news.

ROSS: Good day, good kinsman. How goes the world, sir,
now?
Is't known who did this bloody deed, Macduff?

MACDUFF: Those of his chamber it would seem.

Ross: Alas!

What good could they pretend?

Macduff: They were suborned.

Malcolm and Donalbain, the king's two sons,
Are fled, which puts upon them some suspicion.

Ross: Then 'tis most like the sovereignty will fall
Upon Macbeth.

Macduff: He is already named, and gone to Scone
To be crowned.

Ross: Where is Duncan's body?

Macduff: Carried to Colmekill,
The sacred storehouse of his predecessors.

Ross: Will you to Scone?

Macduff: No, cousin, I'll to Fife.

Ross: Well, I will thither.

God's benison go with you and with those
That would make good of bad, and friends of foes.

Music: *Ominous theme, in and under.*

Narrator: And on their wind-swept heath, the witches
are intent on their magic brews, preparing another
prophecy for Macbeth.

Witches (*In unison*): Double, double, toil and trouble;
Fire burn, and cauldron bubble.

1st Witch: Round about the cauldron go;
In the poisoned entrails throw.

2nd Witch: Fillet of a fenny snake,
In the cauldron boil and bake.

3rd Witch: By the pricking of my thumbs,
Something wicked this way comes.

Macbeth (*Fading on*): How now, you secret, black, and
midnight hags. What is't you do?

Witches (*In unison*): A deed without a name.

MACBETH: Answer me, black women of the night,
  To what I ask you.
1ST WITCH: Speak!
2ND WITCH: Demand!
3RD WITCH: We'll answer. Look!
MACBETH (*In wonderment*): A—a head—with a sword by
  it, rising from the cauldron!
1ST WITCH: He knows thy thought.
  Hear his speech, but say thou naught.
1ST APPARITION: Macbeth! Macbeth! Beware Macduff;
  Beware the Thane of Fife. (*Fading*) Enough!
1ST WITCH: Here's another, Macbeth, more potent than
  the first.
MACBETH (*Amazed*): What bloody child is this?
2ND APPARITION (*A boy's voice*): Be bloody, bold and
  resolute. Laugh to scorn
  The power of man, for none of woman born
  (*Fading*) Shall harm Macbeth.
MACBETH (*Happily*): Then live, Macduff. What need I
  fear of thee?
2ND WITCH: Macbeth! Another apparition comes!
MACBETH: What is this,
  That rises like the issue of a king
  And wears upon his baby-brow the round
  And top of sovereignty?
3RD APPARITION (*Another child*): Macbeth shall never
  vanquished be until
  Great Birnam Wood to high Dunsinane Hill
  Shall come against him.
MACBETH (*Elated*): That will never be.
  Who can impress the forest, bid the tree

Unfix his earth-bound root? But wait—one question
more.

Banquo is in his grave, I've seen to that;

But Fleance, his son, escaped. Say, if you can:

Shall Banquo's issue ever hold the throne?

WITCHES (*Fading, in unison*): Seek to know no more.

MUSIC: *Threatening theme, in and under.*

NARRATOR: Malcolm, prince of the realm and son of the
late King Duncan, having fled to England when his
father's murder was discovered, raises an army with
which to take the throne from Macbeth. Allied with
him are many Scottish nobles, among them Macduff.
Macbeth's army prepares itself for the battle with Malcolm's English troops, but even his own men are secretly
against the murderous Macbeth.

1ST LORD: The English power is near, led on by Malcolm
and Macduff. Revenge burns in them against our kinsman and our king, Macbeth.

2ND LORD: Near Birnam Wood shall the king's army meet
them; that way are they coming. What does the tyrant
king?

1ST LORD: He strongly fortifies the walls of Dunsinane
Castle. Now does he feel his secret murders sticking on
his hands. Well, march we on to give our obedience full
—if not our hearts.

2ND LORD: Our obedience full, or so much as it needs

To dew the sovereign flower and drown the weeds.

MUSIC: *Tragic theme, in and under.*

NARRATOR: Even as the armies are forming to wage battle
over the throne, Lady Macbeth, the ambitious queen
whose evil advice instigated Duncan's murder, is suffer-
ing from remorse for her crimes. Her mind snaps, and

observed by her lady-in-waiting and doctor, she walks in her sleep, confessing her crimes.

DOCTOR: I have two nights watched with you, good Nurse, but can perceive no truth in your reports. When was it she last walked?

NURSE: Since his Majesty went into the field, worthy Doctor, I have seen her rise from her bed, throw her nightgown upon her, unlock her closet, take forth paper, fold it, write upon it, read it, afterwards seal it, and again return to bed; yet all this while in a most fast sleep.

DOCTOR: What, at any time, have you heard her say?

NURSE: That, sir, which I will not report after her. But lo you, here she comes. And upon my life, fast asleep. Observe her and stand close.

DOCTOR: You see her eyes are open.

NURSE: Aye, but their sense is shut. See how she rubs her hands? It is an accustomed action with her, to seem thus washing her hands.

LADY MACBETH (*Slightly off mike, as throughout scene; her mind is wandering*): Yet here's a spot.

DOCTOR: Hark, she speaks! I will set down what comes from her, to satisfy my remembrance the more strongly.

LADY MACBETH: Out, damned spot, out, I say! One, two. Why, then, 'tis time to do't. Fie, my lord, fie! A soldier, and afeard? Yet who would have thought the old man to have so much blood in him?

DOCTOR: Do you mark that?

LADY MACBETH: What, will these hands ne'er be clean? Here's the smell of blood still. All the perfumes of Arabia will not sweeten this little hand. (*Sighing*) Ohhhhhhh!

DOCTOR: What a sigh is there! The heart is sorely charged.

NURSE: I would not have such a heart in my bosom for the dignity of the whole body.

LADY MACBETH: I tell you yet again, my lord, Banquo's buried. He cannot come out of his grave. There's a knocking at the gate. Come, come, give me your hand. What's done cannot be undone. To bed! (*Fading*) Come, my lord, to bed. To bed!

DOCTOR: Foul whisperings are abroad. More needs she the divine than the physician. God, God forgive us all. So good night. My mind she has mated, and amazed my sight. I think, but dare not speak.

NURSE: Good night, good Doctor.

MUSIC: *Theme of battle and conflict, in and under.*

NARRATOR: The battle begins, and from the very start Macbeth's losses are heavy. At last he is forced to barricade himself with a handful of soldiers in his castle. Supported by the witches' prophecy, his courage is high, and he exults in his confidence.

MACBETH (*Commanding*): Bring me no more reports!
Till Birnam Wood remove to Dunsinane,
I cannot taint with fear. Where's the boy Malcolm?
Was he not born of woman? The witches said
"Fear not, Macbeth. No man that's born of woman
Shall e'er have power upon thee."

MESSENGER (*Off mike*): Your Majesty!

MACBETH: What is your news?

MESSENGER: The Queen, my lord, is dead.

MACBETH (*Thoughtfully*): She should have died hereafter;
There would have been a time for such a word.
Go thou, my man, unto the battlements
And bring me news of the approaching army.

MESSENGER (*Fading*): I do, your Majesty.

MACBETH: Tomorrow, and tomorrow, and tomorrow
Creeps in this petty pace from day to day,
To the last syllable of recorded time;
And all our yesterdays have lighted fools
The way to dusty death. Out, out, brief candle!
Life's but a walking shadow, a poor player,
That struts and frets his hour upon the stage
And then is heard no more. It is a tale
Told by an idiot, full of sound and fury,
Signifying nothing.

MESSENGER (*Fading on, breathlessly*): A word, my lord!

MACBETH (*Anxiously*): Thou comest to use thy tongue.
Thy story quickly!

MESSENGER: As I did stand my watch upon the hill,
I looked toward Birnam, and anon methought
The wood began to move.

MACBETH (*Raging*): Liar and slave!
If thou speakst false, on yon tree shalt thou hang.
If thy speech of moving trees be truth,
I care not if thou dost the same for me.
I pull in resolution, and begin
To doubt the equivocation of the fiend
That lies like truth. "Fear not till Birnam Wood
Do come to Dunsinane." And now a wood
Comes to Dunsinane! (*Shouting*) Arm, arm and out!
Ring the alarum bell! Blow, wind! Come, wrack!
At least we'll die with harness on our back.

MUSIC: *Tempestuous theme, in and under.*

NARRATOR: Malcolm's army having disguised their ma-
neuvers with branches chopped from Birnam Wood, the

witches' prophecy about the moving forest has come
true. Malcolm's forces invade the castle, and at last Macbeth is face to face with his hated enemy, Macduff.

SOUND: *Far off, the sounds and cries of battle.*

MACBETH: They have tied me to a stake. I cannot fly,
But bear-like I must fight the course. What's he
That was not born of woman? Such a one
Am I to fear, or none.

MACDUFF (*Off mike, fading on, wildly*): Turn, hell-hound,
turn!

MACBETH: Macduff! Of all men have I avoided thee!
But get thee back! My soul is too much charged
With blood of thine already.

MACDUFF: I have no words. My voice is in my sword.

MACBETH: I bear a charmed life, which must not yield
To one of woman born.

MACDUFF: Despair thy charm!
And let the angel whom thou still hast served
Tell thee Macduff was from his mother's womb
Untimely ripp'd.

MACBETH: Accursed be the tongue that tells me so,
For it hath cowed my better part of man!
I'll not fight with thee!

MACDUFF: Then yield thee, coward.

MACBETH: I will not yield
To kiss the ground before young Malcolm's feet.
Though Birnam Wood be come to Dunsinane,
And thou opposed, being of no woman born,
Yet will I try the last. Before my body
I throw my warlike shield. Lay on, Macduff,
And cursed be he that first cries "Hold, enough!"

MUSIC: *Tragic theme, in and under.*

NARRATOR: As prophesied, Macbeth meets his death at the hand of Macduff, who was not "born of woman." Victoriously, Macduff brings the head of Macbeth before the new king, Malcolm, and the triumphant English army.

SOUND: *Fanfare and drums.*

MACDUFF: Hail, King Malcolm, for so thou art. Behold
The vile usurper Macbeth's cursed head.
The time is free. The victory is ours.
I see thee compassed with thy kingdom's pearl,
That speak my salutation in their minds;
Whose voices I desire aloud with mine—
Hail, Malcolm, King of Scotland!

CHORUS OF MEN (*In unison*): Hail, Malcolm, King of Scotland!

SOUND: *Fanfare.*

CHORUS OF MEN (*In unison*): Hail, Malcolm, King of Scotland!

SOUND: *Fanfare, into . . .*

MUSIC: *Triumphant theme, full to finish.*

THE END

Radio Workshop

Though radio broadcasting is, perhaps, the least formal and rigid of all entertainment media, there are a few basic facts that the radio actor and director must be familiar with to insure a successful show. In the following pages you will find a number of ideas, suggestions, definitions and words of advice that will help to give your program a really professional touch. Once you are equipped with this basic information—information that is used in all commercial radio broadcasting, from the small local stations to the biggest of coast-to-coast networks—you will be able to present smooth, finished, *professional* productions of the scripts in this volume.

WHEN YOU MEET THE MICROPHONE. . . . The radio actor's tools are his intelligence, his voice, and his speech. They are his stock-in-trade, and it is his responsibility to his audience to see that they are in the best possible working order. If you are a newcomer to radio, the following words on "mike technique"—which is just a fancy way of saying how you deliver your lines—will probably prove helpful. First we will discuss your voice, and then your speech, for the two, though related, are very definitely separate and distinct aspects of your delivery.

The effective radio voice is one that sounds *natural*. A voice that is too loud annoys the listener; a too-soft voice strains the listener's ear. Therefore, the wise radio actor uses a voice that is much the same as his own normal, conversational voice. If he is playing a character role, of course, he will need to vary it; but in doing so, he should avoid extreme shrillness or huskiness. In short, he should never go to extremes with his voice. He will also try to please the listener and maintain interest by contrast, pauses, variation and vitality in his voice.

Because the audience of a radio play does not see the speakers, the actor must always use clear, distinct speech. He must pronounce his words carefully, and enunciate distinctly. The most offending speech error made on the air is the explosive—or "popping"—of 's' and 'p' sounds—so watch out for them!

Remember that the most important factor in radio acting is to sound natural. Breathe easily, maintain a distance of twelve to fifteen inches from the mike, and *relax*.

A Few Special Words about Shakespeare. . . . Though at first glance the language of these plays may seem to differ completely from the vocabulary of twentieth century United States, as you read over the speeches you will find that the meanings are clear and the manner of expression natural. Shakespeare was a master with words, and his ideas are always expressed in a vital, articulate, and communicative manner. In delivering your lines, don't pay too much attention to the fact that they may be written in verse; keep in mind what it is your character is saying— what idea he is trying to "get across"—and concentrate on communicating that idea to the listener. Make sure you understand all the words your character uses.

By phrasing carefully, you can make the meaning of your speeches clear, and the rhythm inherent in Shakespeare's dialogue will become a natural and integral part of your speech. Bear in mind that honesty of characterization and believability are what you are striving for, so let each character speak as though he is really thinking about what he is saying, and meaning every word of it!

WHEN YOU ARE THE SOUND TECHNICIAN. . . . Sound effects—especially in dramatic productions—play a very important part in a successful broadcast, because they help the play "come alive" and seem real to the listener. As a result, sound effects must be carefully chosen, diligently timed, and precisely executed. Here are a few rules to guide you, the sound-effects man, in your difficult job.

1. When possible, use the real thing to provide the sound. An actual door being shut will sound more like a real door to the listener than any imitation. This applies to most other usual effects as well.

2. When the real thing is not available, improvise. Use your imagination. For example, while it is not always practical to use a real gun with blanks, or even a cap pistol, a yardstick slapped firmly against a table-top will provide a satisfactory substitute. Your local library will have many books on play-producing for amateurs, which will include notes on other such improvised sound effects: thunder, horses, etc.

3. Many effects—especially natural ones, like wind, rain, etc.—will best be reproduced from professionally-made recordings. These can be purchased from several specialized

recording companies. Also, many radio stations maintain record libraries from which you may be able to borrow the required transcriptions.

4. Make sure all effects are carefully rehearsed and timed, so that they blend in with the play, and do not "stick out" from it; they are a *part* of the play, not a separate entity.

5. And most important, remember that a few good sound effects are far better than many jumbled ones. Use them only when really necessary to enhance the production.

WHEN YOU ARE IN CHARGE OF MUSIC. . . . Music is used to indicate mood, passage of time, change of scene, etc. You will most likely be choosing the music for your radio play from available classical recordings. Try to find selections that will be proper for the time, locale and "feeling" of the production and specific scene. But do not use music that your audience will readily recognize, unless you have a particular reason for doing so. For example, it would not be advisable to use sections of "Peter and the Wolf" in a production of, say, "King Lear," as such music would be inappropriate. On the other hand, the familiar "Rule, Britannia!" would be very useful, should you desire to indicate immediately to your audience that the location of the play is England.

WHEN YOU ARE THE DIRECTOR. . . . As general co-ordinator of the production and arbiter of taste, it is your task to maintain rapport between yourself and the following departments of the production: music, sound, the actors, the announcer, the engineer. You must see that the work of the various departments is carefully integrated into the production without conflict, and that each individual understands what is expected of him. Above all, it is you who will interpret the play itself, guiding your crew along the lines you have set up for them; and in any matter of dispute that arises, it is the director—you—who has final say.

A GLOSSARY OF TERMS. . . . Every craft, trade and profession sets up as a matter of course a new set of words— words which are particularly adapted to its own specific needs. So it is with radio broadcasting. Below is a list of common expressions and terms found in the radio-man's spoken shorthand, which will be invaluable to you in your work in radio, and which will help you to feel right at home behind the mike.

AD LIB: A remark or line which, though rehearsed, has a more informal sound to it than a straight line. Ad libs usually come in groups, different actors speaking different phrases, similar in meaning.

BEAT: A brief, clean-cut pause.

B.G.: Short for "background."

FADE OFF: Used to give the effect of a character's departure, it is accomplished by the actor moving away from the mike while finishing his line.

FADE ON: Used to give the effect of a character approaching, it is accomplished by the actor moving toward the mike while beginning his line.

FILTER: A device, regulated by the engineer, to give strange effects; e.g., telephone voice, conscience, etc. The use of a filter is entirely up to the engineer; the actor uses his normal delivery. (The use of a filter in producing the plays in this book is optional; for productions not given in regular studios, the effect may be completely eliminated, with no detriment to the performance.)

IN AND UNDER: Music beginning from a clean-cut opening point, continuing a few seconds at its given volume, then slowly fading under (behind) the ensuing speech.

MIKE: Short for "microphone."

OUT: Anything thus indicated fades quickly to b.g., then stops.

SCRIPT: The printed (or typewritten) copy of the play.

SEGUE (*pronounced segg-way*): The transition from one musical number to another without any interruption.